Become a facts machine with CGP!

First things first — do you have CGP's KS3 Science Knowledge Organiser? You do? Fantastic!

Now it's time to use this Knowledge Retriever to fetch all those vital KS3 Science facts from your memory, page by page.

There are two tests (one's pretty tricky) for every topic, plus plenty of mixed quizzes to be super sure all that key knowledge has stuck in your brain!

CGP — still the best! ☺

Our sole aim here at CGP is to produce the highest quality books — carefully written, immaculately presented and dangerously close to being funny.

Then we work our socks off to get them out to you — at the cheapest possible prices.

Contents

How to Use This Book............................2

Section 1 — Cells and Respiration

Cells...3

Cell Organisation and Microscopes.............5

Diffusion and Respiration........................7

Mixed Practice Quizzes............................9

Section 2 — Humans as Organisms

Nutrition...11

Digestion...13

The Skeleton and Muscles.......................15

Mixed Practice Quizzes............................17

Gas Exchange..19

Breathing..21

Human Reproduction Systems...................23

Pregnancy and Drugs.............................25

Mixed Practice Quizzes............................27

Section 3 — Plants and Ecosystems

Plant Nutrition......................................29

Plant Reproduction.................................31

Seed Dispersal.......................................33

Dependence on Other Organisms...............35

Mixed Practice Quizzes............................37

Section 4 — Inheritance, Variation and Survival

DNA and Inheritance..............................39

Variation and Natural Selection................41

Extinction and Preserving Species.............43

Mixed Practice Quizzes............................45

Section 5 — Classifying Materials

Solids, Liquids and Gases.......................47

Pressure, Diffusion &
    Changes of State...............................49

Atoms, Elements & the Periodic Table......51

Compounds..53

Mixed Practice Quizzes............................55

Purity and Separating Mixtures.................57

Chromatography and Distillation...............59

Metals and Non-Metals...........................61

Properties of Other Materials....................63

Mixed Practice Quizzes............................65

Section 6 — Chemical Changes

Chemical Reactions and Equations............67

Examples of Chemical Reactions...............69

Acids, Alkalis and Making Salts...............71

Mixed Practice Quizzes............................73

Reactivity of Metals...............................75

Oxides and Displacement Reactions...........77

Mixed Practice Quizzes............................79

Section 7 — The Earth and The Atmosphere

The Earth's Structure..............................81

Rocks..83

Recycling and the Carbon Cycle...............85

The Atmosphere and Climate....................87

Mixed Practice Quizzes............................89

Section 8 — Energy and Matter

Energy Stores and Transfer 91

Energy Transfer 93

Heating 95

Mixed Practice Quizzes 97

Energy Resources 99

Cost of Electricity and Energy Values 101

Physical Changes 103

Movement of Particles 105

Mixed Practice Quizzes 107

Section 9 — Forces and Motion

Speed 109

Forces and Movement 111

Force Diagrams 113

Frictional Forces and Moments 115

Forces and Elasticity 117

Pressure 119

Mixed Practice Quizzes 121

Section 10 — Waves

Water Waves 123

Light Waves and Reflection 125

Refraction, Lenses and Cameras 127

Colour 129

Mixed Practice Quizzes 131

Sound Waves 133

Hearing 135

Uses of Sound Waves 137

Mixed Practice Quizzes 139

Section 11 — Electricity and Magnetism

Electric Current &
    Potential Difference 141

Resistance and Circuit Symbols 143

Series and Parallel Circuits 145

Static Electricity and Magnets 147

Magnetic Fields and Electromagnets 149

Mixed Practice Quizzes 151

Section 12 — The Earth and Beyond

Gravity, The Sun, Stars &
    Light Years 153

Day and Night and the Four Seasons 155

Mixed Practice Quizzes 157

Published by CGP.
From original material by Richard Parsons and Paddy Gannon.

Editors: Emma Clayton, Luke Molloy, Rachael Rogers and George Wright.

ISBN: 978 1 78908 724 6

Printed by Elanders Ltd, Newcastle upon Tyne.
Clipart from Corel®
Illustrations by: Sandy Gardner Artist, email sandy@sandygardner.co.uk

How to Use This Book

Every page in this book has a matching page in the KS3 Science **Knowledge Organiser**.
Before using this book, try to **memorise** everything on a Knowledge Organiser page.
Then follow these **seven steps** to see how much knowledge you're able to retrieve...

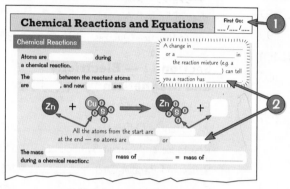

1 In this book, there are two versions of each page. Find the **'First Go'** of the page you've tried to memorise, and write the **date** at the top.

2 Use what you've learned from the Knowledge Organiser to **fill in** any dotted lines or white spaces.

You may need to draw, complete or add labels to diagrams too.

3 Use the Knowledge Organiser to **check your work**.
Use a **different colour pen** to write in anything you missed or that wasn't quite right.
This lets you see clearly what you **know** and what you **don't know**.

4 After doing the First Go page, **wait a few days**. This is important because **spacing out** your retrieval practice helps you to remember things better.

5 Now do the **Second Go** page.
The Second Go page is harder — it has more things missing.

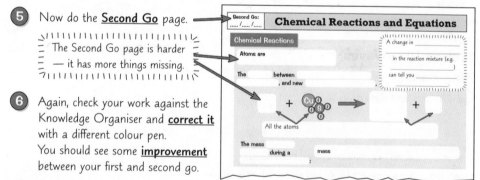

6 Again, check your work against the Knowledge Organiser and **correct it** with a different colour pen.
You should see some **improvement** between your first and second go.

7 **Wait** another few days, then try recreating the whole Knowledge Organiser page on a **blank piece of paper**. If you can do this, you'll know you've **really learned it**.

There are also **Mixed Practice Quizzes** dotted throughout the book:
• The quizzes come in sets of four. They test a mix of content from the previous few pages.
• Do each quiz on a different day — write the date you do each one at the top of the quiz.
• Tick the questions you get right and record your score in the box at the end.

Cells

First Go:
15./.6./22.

An Animal Cell

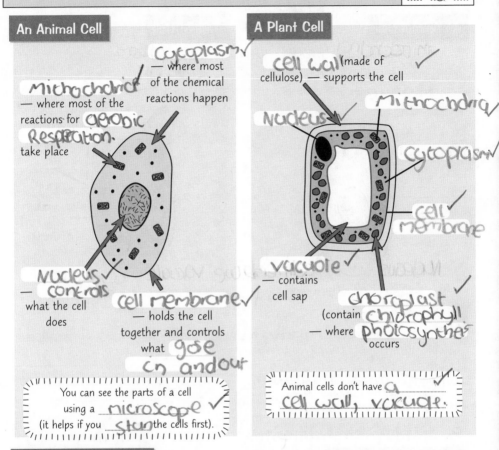

Cytoplasm ✓
— where most of the chemical reactions happen

Mitochondria — where most of the reactions for **aerobic Respiration** take place

Nucleus ✓ — **controls** what the cell does

cell membrane ✓ — holds the cell together and controls what **goes in and out**

You can see the parts of a cell using a **microscope** ✓ (it helps if you **stain** the cells first).

A Plant Cell

cell wall (made of cellulose) — supports the cell ✓

Mitochondria ✓

Nucleus

Cytoplasm ✓

cell membrane ✓

vacuole ✓ — contains cell sap

chloroplast ✓ (contain **chlorophyll**) — where **photosynthesis** occurs

Animal cells don't have **a** ✓ **cell wall, vacuole.**

Unicellular Organisms

UNICELLULAR ORGANISM — a living thing **all made up of only one cell**

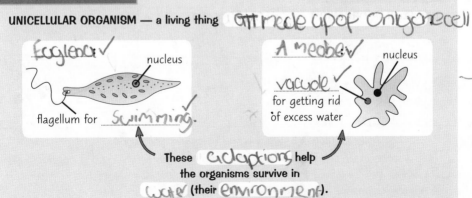

Euglena ✓

nucleus

flagellum for **swimming.** ✓

Amoeba ✓

nucleus

vacuole ✓ for getting rid of excess water

These **adaptations** help the organisms survive in **water** (their **environment**).

Cells

An Animal Cell

Cytoplasm

mitochondria where
where nos most of
Of the react-
ions of areobic
£ respiration
takes place

where most of
the chemical
reactions happen

Nucleus
Controls
what the
cell does

holds the
cell together
and controls
what gose in and out

cell membrane

You can see the parts of a cell
a microscope it helps
if you stain the
cells first

A Plant Cell

cytoplasm
cell wall

Nuclear

mitochondria

cloro
plast
cytoplus

cell
membr
brane

vacoule
contains
cell sap

cytoplasm
chorplast

you animal cells
don't have a
cell wall vacoale

Unicellular Organisms

UNICELLULAR ORGANISM — also known as an organism that
consist of single cell

Euglena

Euglena

FK

nmoeba

These adaptations help the

Cell Organisation and Microscopes

Cell Organisation

'CELL — the basic building block that *make* *Organelle* all living organisms.

tissue — a group of similar cells working together. ✓

organ — a group of similar cells working together ✓

organ sytems — a group of organs working together. ✓

Organ systems work together to *organism.* ✓

organ systems work together ✓ *tomciko* are usually made up of several organ systems.

A Microscope

Eyepiece ✓

rough ✓ focusing knob

Objective lenses *(choose* (*Slide* lens is *stage oic* powered) ✓ ✓

find focusing knob ✓

Sistage holder hanoie

Hole

Slide ✓

higher and low power objective lense

Mirror ✓

Using a Microscope

Angle mirror so *light so light shines* in stage. ✓

Clip slide onto stase ✓

Start with *slowest powered* ✓ objective lens and move it down to just above slide by turning ✓ *rough fousing kind* ✓

Look down *eyepiece* and adjust focus with _____ until you get a _____ of what's on slide.

To see slide with a _____
_____, swap to
_____
_____ lens and refocus.

Cell Organisation and Microscopes

Cell Organisation

organele

CELL — the basic building *block that ~ all living orgu*

↓

tissue a *group oof similar cells*

↓

working together

Organs *a group of organs*

working together

↓

Organ systems — a *Organs* working together.

↓

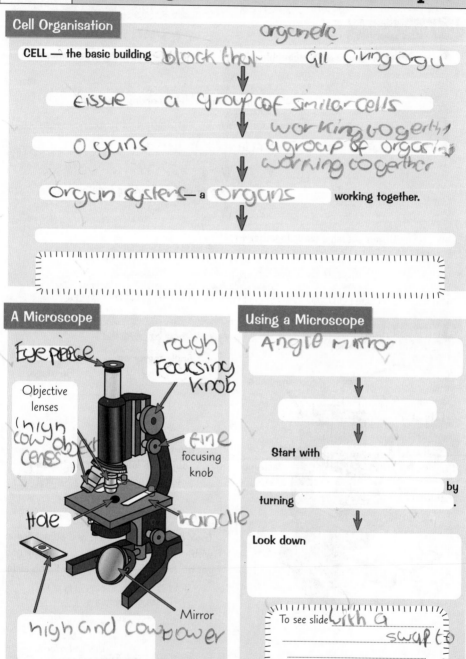

A Microscope

Eyepeece

Objective lenses

(high cow objective lenses)

rough Focusing Knob

fine focusing knob

Hole

handle

high and cow power

Mirror

Using a Microscope

Angle mirror

↓

↓

Start with

by

turning   .

↓

Look down

To see slide *with a swap to*

and refocus.

7

Diffusion and Respiration

Diffusion

DIFFUSION — the process of substances spreading out from _an area of_ _higer concetra_ .

Substances that cells need (e.g. _____) move ____ cells by diffusion. Waste products (e.g. _____) move ____ of cells by diffusion.

glucose

Respiration

RESPIRATION — the process of _____ . It's a chemical reaction that happens _____ _____ .

The energy released is used for _____ , such as:

- _____
- keeping warm.
- building _____ .

Aerobic Respiration

AEROBIC RESPIRATION — _Occurs in presence_ .

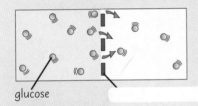

glucose + _oxygen_ ⟶ carbon dioxide + _Nciter_ (+ _Aerobic_)

Anaerobic Respiration

ANAEROBIC RESPIRATION — _____ .

Anaerobic respiration releases _____ than aerobic respiration.

In humans (_____):

glucose ⟶ _____ (+ energy)

_____ when it builds up in muscles.

In microorganisms _____ :

glucose ⟶ _____ + _____ (+ energy)

This process is called _____ . It's used to make _____ .

 ☑ ☑ ☑

| Second Go:
..... /..... /..... | # Diffusion and Respiration |

Diffusion

DIFFUSION — the process of substances

Substances that cells need (e.g.

Respiration

RESPIRATION —

It's a chemical reaction that happens

The energy released

-
-
- building

Aerobic Respiration

AEROBIC RESPIRATION — ....

.... + ... ➡ .... + ... (+ ....)

Anaerobic Respiration

ANAEROBIC RESPIRATION —
....

Anaerobic respiration ....
....

.... ➡ .... (+ energy)

.... ➡ .... + ... (+ energy)

This process is called

Section 1 — Cells and Respiration

Mixed Practice Quizzes

Well done — that's Section 1 almost over. All there is left to do is these quizzes — they should test how much has stuck in your head from p.3-8.

Quiz 1 Date: ...... / ...... / ......

1) What type of respiration uses oxygen? ~~are~~ aerobic cellular ✓
2) What is a tissue? A group cells that function together ✓
3) List three parts of a cell that are found in plant cells but not in animal cells. ✓
   Nucleus, cell membrane, cytoplasm
4) Describe one situation where humans might start respiring anaerobically. ✓
   Intensity exercise
5) Name the part of a microscope that you put the slide on. ✓
   stage
6) What is the word equation for anaerobic respiration in yeast cells? ✓
   glucose - ethanol + carbon CO_2 + energy
7) What is the fine focusing knob of a microscope
   used for when looking at an object on a slide. ✓
8) True or false? When substances diffuse, they move from an
   area of lower concentration to an area of higher concentration. ✓

Total: 7

Quiz 2 Date: ...... / ...... / ......

1) When using a microscope, what should you do if you
   want to see the slide with a greater magnification? ✓
2) What is the word equation for anaerobic respiration in humans? ✓
   glucose + enzymes carbon dioxied ethanyl
3) What is a unicellular organism? ✓
   A unicellor is a organism coctic acid consists of a single
4) Give one way in which anaerobic respiration cell ✓
   in microorganisms is used by humans.
5) True or false? Cells are the basic building ✓
   blocks that make up all living organisms.
6) Name the two types of focusing knobs found on a microscope. ✓
   rough fine
7) Which type of respiration releases more energy? aerobic ✓
   respiration
8) Define 'diffusion'.

Total:

Section 1 — Cells and Respiration

Mixed Practice Quizzes

Quiz 3   Date: ...... / ...... / ......

1) What is the word equation for aerobic respiration?

2) When using a microscope, what should you do with the mirror before you look at the slide?

3) What is an organ?

4) True or false? Fermentation happens when microorganisms respire anaerobically.

5) Name a unicellular organism and describe one way in which it's adapted to survive in its environment.

6) Define 'respiration'.

7) Which part of a cell controls what the cell does?

8) What are the functions of a cell membrane?

Total:

Quiz 4   Date: ...... / ...... / ......

1) Describe why anaerobic respiration can cause pain in humans.

2) What is an organ system?

3) In what part of a plant cell does photosynthesis occur?

4) Which type of respiration doesn't use oxygen?

5) When using a microscope, should you start with the lowest powered or highest powered lens?

6) Name the two products of aerobic respiration.

7) What name is given to the process in which energy is released from glucose inside cells?

8) What is the function of these cell parts:
a) cell wall,   b) mitochondria,   c) cytoplasm?

Total:

Nutrition

Seven Components of a Healthy Diet

	Component	Needed For
1	Carbohydrates	
2		Cell _____ and repair
3	Lipids (____ and ____)	Energy (used if _____ run out)
4	Vitamins	Vital _____ in the body
5		E.g. ____ for healthy blood, ____ for strong teeth and bones
6	Fibre	Moving food through _____
7	Water	All _____ in body

Energy Requirements

BASIC ENERGY REQUIREMENT (BER) — energy needed
to _____ .

in _____

Daily BER =
5.4 × 24 × _____
in kg

_____ needed in a day =
_____ + extra energy for activities

The _____ and more _____ you are,
the more energy _____ .

Three Possible Effects of an Unbalanced Diet

	Effect	Caused by	Possible consequences
1	Obesity (weighing over _____ than the _____ weight for _____)	Taking in _____ from food than is _____ .	_____ problems, e.g. high _____ pressure, heart _____ .
2		Lack of food.	Slow _____ , greater risk of _____ , irregular _____ .
3	_____ diseases E.g. lack of _____ can cause scurvy.	Lack of _____ or _____ .	E.g. scurvy leads to _____ with skin, _____ and _____ .

 ☑   ☑   ☑

Nutrition

Seven Components of a Healthy Diet

	Component	Needed For
1		
2		Cell
3	Lipids	Energy (used if)
4	Vitamins	in the body
5		E.g. for healthy , for strong
6	Fibre	food through
7		

Energy Requirements

BASIC ENERGY REQUIREMENT (BER) —

in

_____ =

5.4 × 24 × _____

in

_____ needed in _____ =
_____ +
extra _____

The _____ _____ you are, the _____ _____.

Three Possible Effects of an Unbalanced Diet

Effect	Caused by	Possible consequences
1 Obesity (weighing than the)	Taking in	, e.g. high , heart .
2	Lack of .	, greater , irregular .
3 diseases E.g. lack of can cause .	Lack of	E.g. scurvy leads to

Digestion

The Digestive System

DIGESTION — the process of [_____]
so the [_____] can be absorbed into the [_____].

ENZYMES — biological [_____] (things that
[_____] chemical [_____] in the body).

2 Oesophagus ([_____])

1 Mouth
• Teeth [_____].
• Saliva contains [_____] —
  an enzyme that breaks down [_____].

3 [_____]
• Muscular tissue [_____] food.
• Contains protease [_____]
  that break down [_____].
• Acid [_____] bacteria.

4 [_____]
Makes bile, which
breaks [____] into [_____]

5 Pancreas ⎤ Make [_____]
                  ⎟ that break down
                  ⎟ carbohydrates,
6 [_____] ⎟ [_____]
intestine ⎦ and [_____].

8 Rectum
Stores undigested food
as [_____], which leaves
through [_____].

7 [_____] intestine
[_____] absorbed into blood.

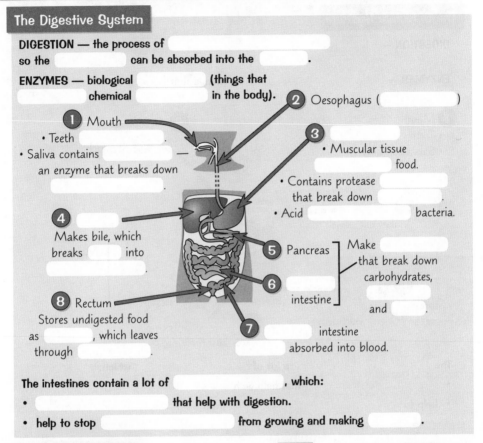

The intestines contain a lot of [_____], which:
• [_____] that help with digestion.
• help to stop [_____] from growing and making [_____].

Absorption of Food

Food is absorbed in the [_____].

[____] food molecules can't
pass through [_____]. [_____] food
molecules can
pass through [_____]

break them
down

Blood

[_____]

Molecules travel
to [_____]

Villi

Villi line the [_____].
Three [_____] of villi
that make them [_____] to
food absorption:

1 Thin outer [_____]
of cells [_____]

2 Good [_____]
supply

3 [_____] surface
area

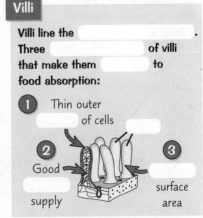

Second Go:
...../...../.....

Digestion

The Digestive System

DIGESTION —

ENZYMES — (things that).

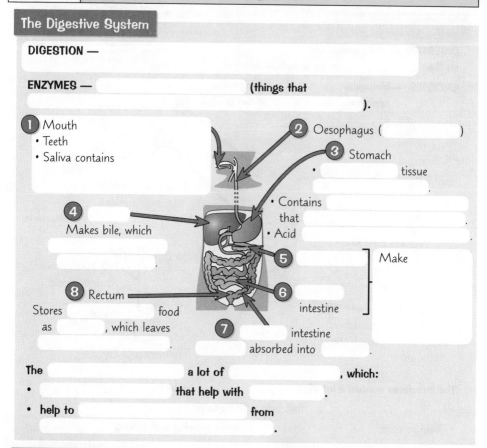

1. Mouth
   - Teeth
   - Saliva contains

2. Oesophagus ( )

3. Stomach
   - tissue
   - Contains that
   - Acid

4. Makes bile, which

5.

6. intestine

7. intestine absorbed into

8. Rectum
   Stores food as , which leaves

Make

The a lot of , which:
- that help with
- help to from

Absorption of Food

Food is in the .

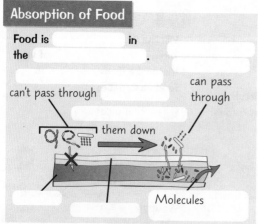

can't pass through

can pass through

them down

Molecules

Villi

Villi
Three

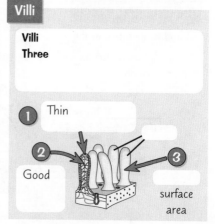

1. Thin

2. Good

3. surface area

The Skeleton and Muscles

The Skeleton

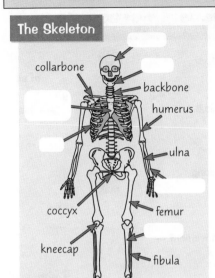

collarbone

backbone

humerus

ulna

coccyx

femur

kneecap

fibula

Four Functions of the Skeleton

1 Protection of
_____ — e.g.
the skull protects
_____ .

2 Support of all
the body's
_____ — this
allows us to
_____ .

3 Making _____ —
bone _____ makes red
and _____ .

4 Movement —
_____ allow the skeleton _____ .

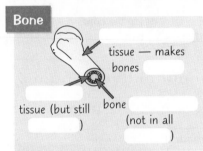

_____ (connects
_____ to bone)

_____ muscle — when it
_____ , it
applies a _____
to the bone, making
bone _____

You can use your knowledge of
_____ to work out
_____ by a
muscle (the joint is the _____).

Bone

_____

tissue — makes
bones _____

_____ bone

tissue (but still _____)

(not in all _____)

Antagonistic Muscles

ANTAGONISTIC MUSCLES — _____ that
work _____ each other, e.g. the _____ .

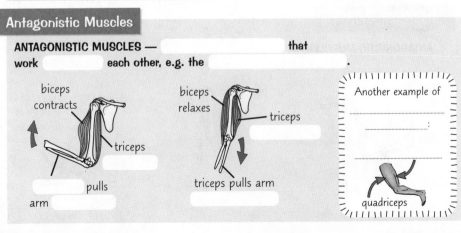

biceps
contracts

triceps

_____ pulls
arm

biceps
relaxes

triceps

triceps pulls arm

Another example of
_____
_____ :
_____

quadriceps

 ☑ ☑ ☑

The Skeleton and Muscles

The Skeleton

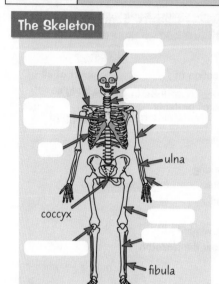

ulna

coccyx

fibula

Four Functions of the Skeleton

1
— e.g.
the skull

2
of all
the body's
— this
.

3 Making ___ —
makes
.

4 Movement —
— when it
, it
to the bone,

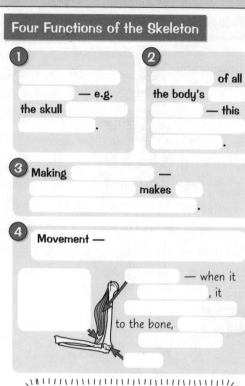

You can use _____
_____ to work out
_____
muscle (the _____ is the _____).

Bone

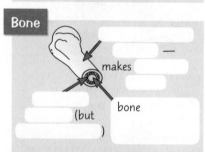

makes —

bone

(but
)

Antagonistic Muscles

ANTAGONISTIC MUSCLES —

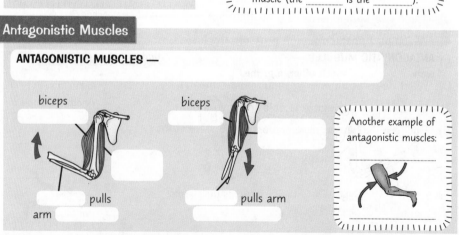

biceps

biceps

pulls
arm

pulls arm

Another example of
antagonistic muscles:

Section 2 — Humans as Organisms

Mixed Practice Quizzes

It's time for some quizzes to see how much you've digested from p.11-16.
Don't forget to tick the questions you get right and add up your score.

Quiz 1   Date: ...... / ...... / ......

1) True or false? Enzymes slow down chemical reactions in the body.

2) Why are: a) proteins needed in the diet? b) vitamins needed in the diet?

3) Why is saliva important for digestion?

4) Give four functions of the skeleton.

5) To work out the total amount of energy you need in a day,
   what two things do you need to add together?

6) Give an example of a pair of antagonistic muscles in the body.

7) In which part of the digestive system is faeces stored?

8) How is obesity caused?

Total:

Quiz 2   Date: ...... / ...... / ......

1) Describe three functions of the stomach.

2) Name the structure that connects a muscle to a bone.

3) Name two components of a healthy diet that provide energy.

4) Which part of the skeleton protects the brain?

5) Describe how the lining of the small intestine is adapted for absorption.

6) What does 'basic energy requirement' mean?

7) Describe how a muscle is able to move a bone.

8) How are deficiency diseases caused?

Total:

Mixed Practice Quizzes

Date: ...... / ...... / ......

1) Name two bones found in the arm.
2) State three possible consequences of starvation.
3) What are the seven components of a healthy diet?
4) What is the function of bone marrow?
5) What is iron needed for in the body?
6) Where is bile produced?
7) True or false? Small food molecules are absorbed
   from the small intestine into the blood.
8) What are antagonistic muscles?

Total:

Quiz 4   Date: ...... / ...... / ......

1) True or false? The outer layer of bone is made from strong, hard tissue.
2) Name two parts of the digestive system that
   make enzymes that break down fats.
3) Why is it important to get fibre in your diet?
4) Why is bile important in digestion?
5) Name two bones found in the leg.
6) What is the formula for calculating daily basic energy requirement?
7) Explain how the biceps and triceps work together to move the arm down.
8) Give two benefits of the bacteria found in the intestines.

Total:

Gas Exchange

Gas Exchange System

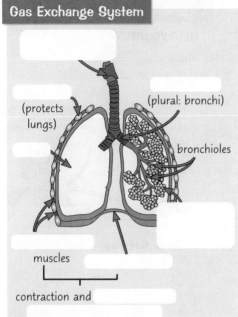

(protects lungs)

(plural: bronchi)

bronchioles

muscles

contraction and

Lung Volume

LUNG VOLUME —

in a single breath.

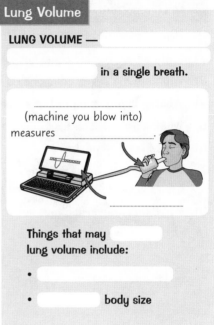

(machine you blow into)
measures

Things that may
lung volume include:

•

• body size

Gas Exchange in Alveoli

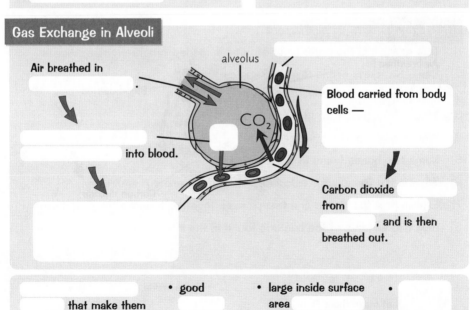

alveolus

Air breathed in

into blood.

CO_2

Blood carried from body cells —

Carbon dioxide from

, and is then breathed out.

that make them
suited to gas exchange:

• good

• large inside surface area

•

 ☑ ☑ ☑

Gas Exchange

Gas Exchange System

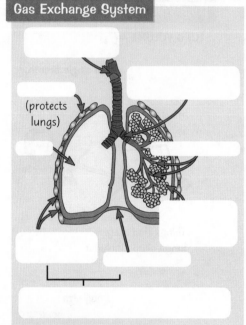

(protects lungs)

Lung Volume

LUNG VOLUME —

Things that may [   ]:

- [   ]
- [   ]

Gas Exchange in Alveoli

Air breathed in

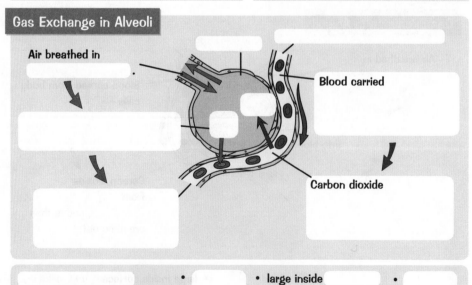

Blood carried

Carbon dioxide

[   ] that make them suited to [   ]:

- large inside

Breathing

Breathing In and Out

air drawn ___

IN

volume of chest cavity ___,

so ___

diaphragm ___
(so moves down)

___ (so ribs move up and out)

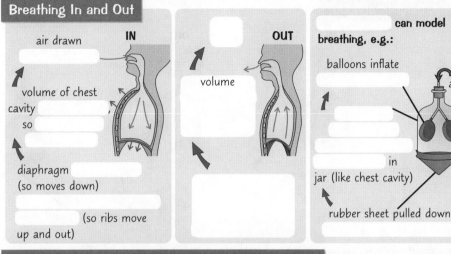

OUT

volume ___

___ can model breathing, e.g.:

balloons inflate

___

___ in jar (like chest cavity)

air

rubber sheet pulled down

Three Things That Affect the Gas Exchange System

1 Exercise

Breathing ___ increase during exercise.

Regular exercise:

- strengthens ___

  (meaning more air can get into lungs)

- increases ___ of small blood vessels in lungs

- ___

These make gas exchange ___ .

2 ___

A person with ___ has lungs that are sensitive to certain things (e.g. dust). Breathing these in ___:

bronchiole

muscle contracts so ___

___ in airway

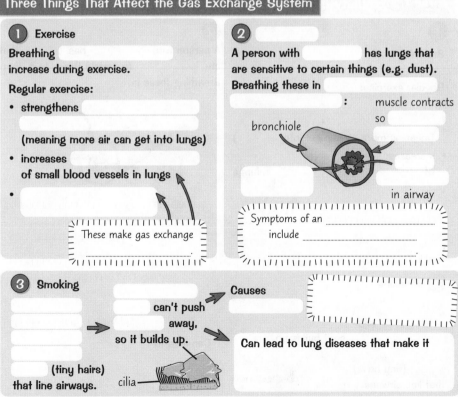

Symptoms of an ___ include ___ ___ .

3 Smoking

___ can't push ___ away, so it builds up.

___ (tiny hairs) that line airways.

cilia

Causes ___

Can lead to lung diseases that make it ___

 ☹ ✓   😐 ✓   😊 ✓

Breathing

Breathing In and Out

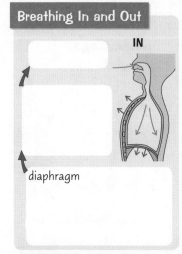

IN

diaphragm

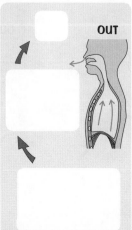

OUT

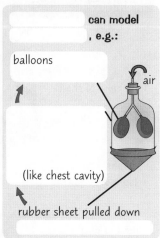

can model
, e.g.:

balloons

air

(like chest cavity)

rubber sheet pulled down

Three Things That Affect the Gas Exchange System

**① **

Breathing

Regular exercise:

*

  (meaning more air can get into   )

* increases
  of   in lungs

*

**② **

A person with   has   that
are   to certain things (e.g. dust).
Breathing these in
                     :

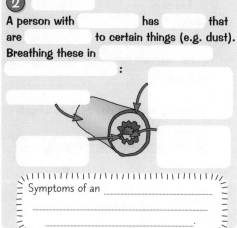

Symptoms of an _____
_____
_____.

③ Smoking

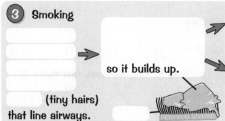

so it builds up.

        (tiny hairs)
that line airways.

Can lead to

Human Reproduction Systems

Male Reproductive System

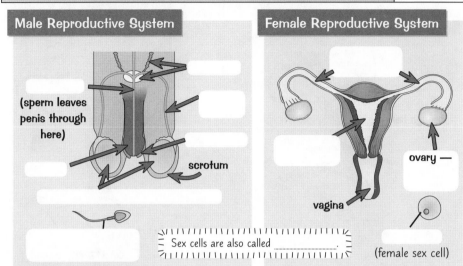

(sperm leaves penis through here)

scrotum

Female Reproductive System

ovary —

vagina

Sex cells are also called ....

(female sex cell)

The Menstrual Cycle

MENSTRUAL CYCLE — monthly sequence of events (after puberty) that

....

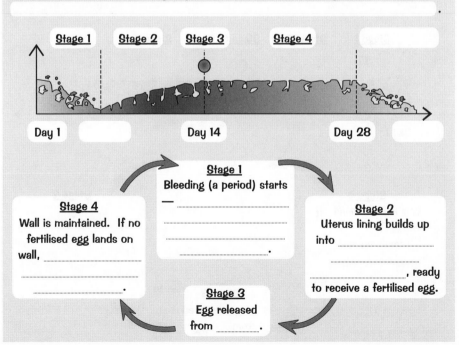

Stage 1   Stage 2   Stage 3   Stage 4

Day 1   Day 14   Day 28

Stage 1
Bleeding (a period) starts
— ....
....
....
....

Stage 2
Uterus lining builds up
into ....
....
...., ready
to receive a fertilised egg.

Stage 3
Egg released
from ....

Stage 4
Wall is maintained. If no
fertilised egg lands on
wall, ...
....
....

 ✓   ✓   ✓

Second Go:
..... / ..... / .....

Human Reproduction Systems

Male Reproductive System

through here)

Female Reproductive System

(female   )

The Menstrual Cycle

MENSTRUAL CYCLE —

Stage 1   Stage 2   Stage 3   Stage 4

Day 1

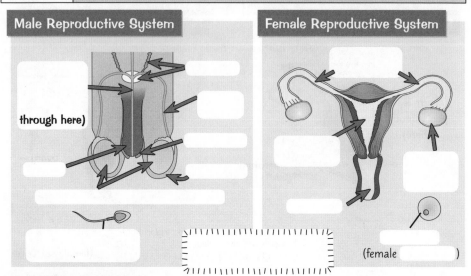

Stage 1

Stage 2

Stage 4
Wall is maintained. If
no ....
        lands on wall,

....

....

....

Stage 3
.... released
from ....

Pregnancy and Drugs

Fertilisation and Development

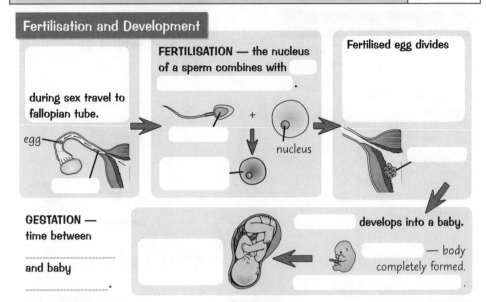

during sex travel to fallopian tube.

egg

FERTILISATION — the nucleus of a sperm combines with

nucleus

Fertilised egg divides

+

GESTATION — time between

....
and baby
....

develops into a baby.

— body completely formed.

The Placenta

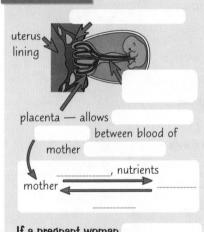

uterus lining

placenta — allows

between blood of

mother

.................., nutrients

mother

....

If a pregnant woman

then some harmful chemicals can cross the placenta, which can affect the

.

Drugs

DRUG — anything that   the body works.

— drug used for

.

They can be   ...or
(e.g.   )...   (e.g. heroin).

Three things that ....
.... can affect:

1

2   — e.g. drugs affecting the brain can affect movement and   .

3 Behaviour — e.g. they can make people feel

. Many are addictive.

Pregnancy and Drugs

Fertilisation and Development

during sex travel to fallopian tube.

FERTILISATION —

Fertilised egg

+

GESTATION —

....
....
....
....

develops into a ....

completely formed.

The Placenta

placenta —

If a pregnant woman

Drugs

DRUG —

They can

Three things ....
.... :

1

2 affecting the brain can affect movement
....

3 Behaviour — e.g.

Mixed Practice Quizzes

There's no doubting that reproducing science-based facts is hard work. It's time to find out how much you've learnt from p.19-26 by doing some quiz questions.

Quiz 1 Date: ...... / ...... / ......

1) What are female gametes called?
2) Give three ways that regular exercise affects the gas exchange system.
3) Describe the function of the placenta.
4) Describe where the diaphragm is found in the gas exchange system.
5) True or false? Sperm leaves the penis through the urethra.
6) State two things that may reduce lung volume.
7) Around what day of the menstrual cycle is an egg released from an ovary?
8) What happens to oxygen in the air that enters alveoli?

Total:

Quiz 2 Date: ...... / ...... / ......

1) Why are women advised not to smoke during pregnancy?
2) What is the name of the tube that carries air into the bronchi?
3) Name the part of the male reproductive system where sperm is made.
4) What can be used to measure lung volume?
5) In the menstrual cycle, what happens if no fertilised egg lands on the uterus wall?
6) What happens to the diaphragm when breathing out?
7) Where does an embryo implant before it develops into a foetus?
8) What is meant by: a) a drug? b) a recreational drug?

Total:

Mixed Practice Quizzes

Quiz 3   Date: ...... / ...... / ......

1) Name the small tubes that connect the bronchi to the alveoli. ☑
2) What part of the female reproductive system makes eggs? ☑
3) Why does smoking cause mucus to build up in the airways? ☑
4) Give an example of a legal recreational drug and
   describe how using it could affect your health. ☑
5) Give three ways that the lungs are adapted for gas exchange. ☑
6) Describe how carbon dioxide from respiration
   leaves the body via the gas exchange system. ☑
7) Explain how a bell jar, rubber sheet and balloons can model breathing in. ☑
8) What does 'gestation' mean? ☑

Total: ☐

Quiz 4   Date: ...... / ...... / ......

1) What does 'lung volume' mean? ☑
2) Name the part of the female reproductive system
   that links the ovaries to the uterus. ☑
3) Describe what happens to the bronchioles during an asthma attack. ☑
4) True or false? All recreational drugs are illegal. ☑
5) Explain how air is pushed out of the lungs when breathing out. ☑
6) What happens during fertilisation? ☑
7) In what part of the lungs does gas exchange take place? ☑
8) How many days does the menstrual cycle last? ☑

Total: ☐

Plant Nutrition

Photosynthesis

PHOTOSYNTHESIS — [⬜⬜⬜⬜⬜⬜] in which [⬜⬜⬜⬜⬜⬜] use energy from [⬜⬜⬜⬜] to make [⬜⬜⬜⬜⬜⬜].

carbon dioxide + water ——————⟶ .... + ...

Four things needed for [⬜⬜⬜⬜⬜] :

1 [⬜⬜⬜⬜⬜]

2 [⬜⬜⬜⬜⬜] (green chemical in chloroplasts which absorbs [⬜⬜⬜⬜⬜])

3 [⬜⬜⬜⬜] (from soil)

4 [⬜⬜⬜⬜⬜] (from air)

Four Adaptations of Leaves for Photosynthesis

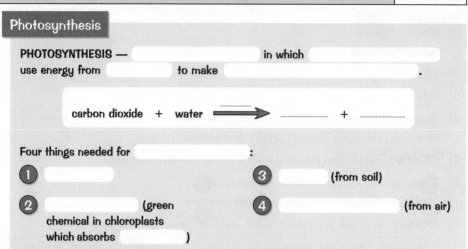

1 Big surface area for [⬜⬜⬜⬜⬜].

2 [⬜⬜⬜⬜⬜] mostly near [⬜⬜] of leaf for more [⬜⬜⬜].

3 Veins deliver [⬜⬜⬜⬜⬜] to cells and take [⬜⬜⬜⬜⬜] away.

4 Stomata (small holes) for [⬜⬜⬜⬜⬜].

.... in   .... out

Roots

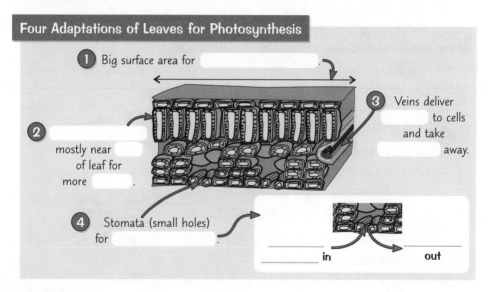

Roots absorb:
• [⬜⬜⬜⬜⬜]
• [⬜⬜⬜⬜⬜]

Plants need [⬜⬜⬜⬜⬜] from soil to [⬜⬜⬜⬜⬜].

Second Go: ...... /...... /......	**Plant Nutrition**

Photosynthesis

PHOTOSYNTHESIS —

_____ + _____ ⟶ _____ + _____

Four things [   ]:

1.

3.

2.

4.

Four Adaptations of Leaves for Photosynthesis

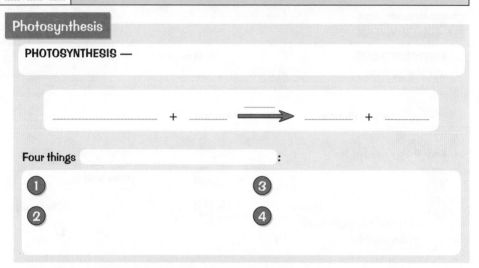

1. Big

2.

mostly near

3. Veins

4. Stomata

Roots

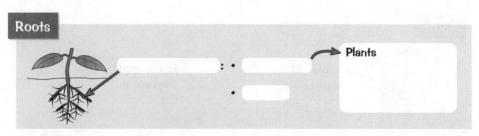

Plants

     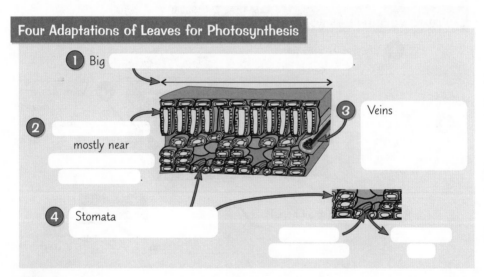

Plant Reproduction

Parts of a Flower

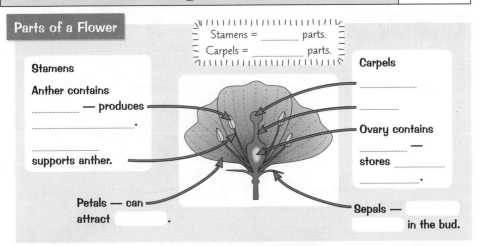

Stamens = ... parts.
Carpels = ... parts.

Stamens

Anther contains
.... — produces
....

....
supports anther.

Petals — can
attract ....

Carpels

....
....

Ovary contains

.... —
stores ....
....

Sepals —
.... in the bud.

Pollination

POLLINATION — ....
.... from stamen to stigma.

Pollen can be ....
from one plant to another,
e.g. by ....

Flowers can have different ....
depending on whether they're .... :

Insect	Wind
.... petals	.... petals
.... sugary flowers	No ....
Anthers .... the flower	.... anthers on long ....
.... stigmas take pollen from	.... stigmas catch pollen

Fertilisation

FERTILISATION — when two
sex cell ....

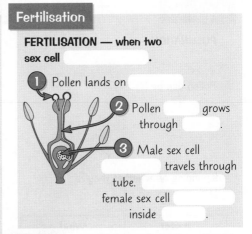

1 Pollen lands on ....

2 Pollen .... grows
through ....

3 Male sex cell
.... travels through
tube.
female sex cell ....
inside ....

Seeds

A seed forms from .... ovule.

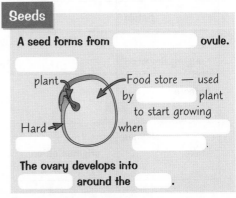

....
plant

Food store — used
by .... plant
to start growing
when ....

Hard ....
....

The ovary develops into
.... around the ....

Second Go:
...../...../.....

Plant Reproduction

Parts of a Flower

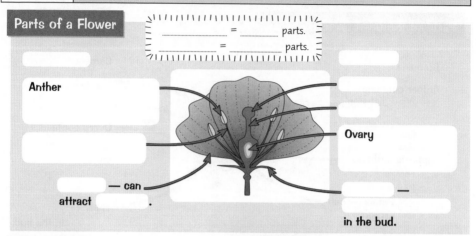

.... = ... parts.
.... = ... parts.

Anther

— can ——
attract [   ] .

Ovary

— [   ] —

in the bud.

Pollination

POLLINATION —

Pollen can be

depending on whether they're

:

Insect	Wind
[ ] petals	
sugary flowers	
Anthers [ ]	
[ ] stigmas take [ ]	stigmas catch pollen

Fertilisation

FERTILISATION —

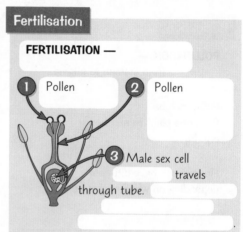

1 Pollen

2 Pollen

3 Male sex cell travels through tube.

.

Seeds

A seed forms from [   ] .

Food store —

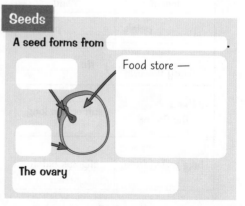

The ovary

 ✓ ✓ ✓

Seed Dispersal

Four Methods of Seed Dispersal

Seeds disperse (...........) so plants grow
with .... from each other.

1 Wind dispersal
.... or ....
help seeds ....

2 Explosion
Seeds ....

3 .... dispersal
Fruit .... — ....
.... in animals' poo.
.... catch
animals' ....

4 Drop and roll
Fruit hits .... and splits
— seeds ....

Two Ways to Investigate Seed Dispersal

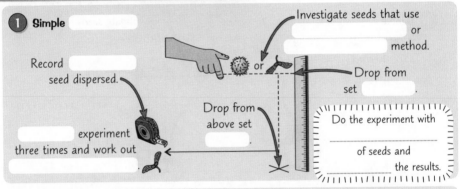

1 Simple ....

Investigate seeds that use
.... or
.... method.

Record ....
seed dispersed.

Drop from
set ....

Drop from
above set ....

Do the experiment with
....
of seeds and
.... the results.

.... experiment
three times and work out
....

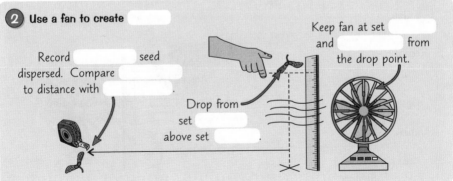

2 Use a fan to create ....

Keep fan at set ....
and .... from
the drop point.

Record .... seed
dispersed. Compare
to distance with ....

Drop from
set ....
above set ....

You must keep some things .... each time you .... an experiment (e.g. ....
dropping the seed, ... it's dropped from) to make sure it's a ....

Seed Dispersal

Four Methods of Seed Dispersal

Seeds .... so plants
grow ....
....

1 ....
....

2 ....
Seeds ....

3 ....

Fruit ....

.... catch
animals' ....

4 ....

Fruit hits ....

Two Ways to Investigate Seed Dispersal

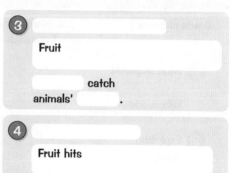

1 Simple ....

Record ....

Investigate seeds

....
three times and ....
Drop
Drop ....
Drop ....

2 Use ....

Keep fan ....

Record ....

Drop from ....

You must .... each time ....
.... (e.g. .... the seed,
.......................) to make sure it's a ....

 ☑ ☑ ☑

Dependence on Other Organisms

Ecosystems

ECOSYSTEM — all the [____] [____] in an area, plus their [____].

[____] in an ecosystem are [____] — they need each other to [____] (so a change in one [____] could easily [____] others).

E.g. many [____] depend on [____] to pollinate them.

Humans also depend on [____] — they pollinate [____] plants, which ensures our [____].

Dependence on Plants

Almost all [____] on Earth depends [____].

Plants use [____] to make food.

⬇

They use food to make [____] like proteins in [____].

⬇

Energy in these [____] is passed on when [____].

Plants produce [____], which all [____] need.

Plants take in [____], which helps to [____] in atmosphere getting [____].

Food Chains

Food chains show how [____] passes between [____].

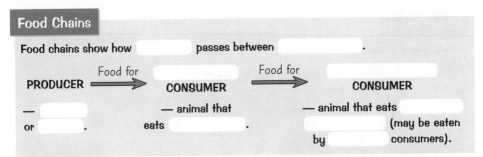

PRODUCER →(Food for)→ CONSUMER →(Food for)→ CONSUMER

— [____] or [____].

— animal that eats [____].

— animal that eats [____] (may be eaten by [____] consumers).

Food Webs

Food webs show [____] linked together. They highlight [____].

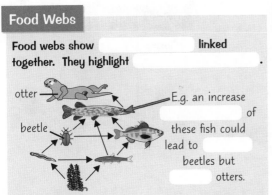

otter

beetle

E.g. an increase [____] of these fish could lead to [____] beetles but [____] otters.

Toxins in Food Chains

Toxins ([____]) can [____] as they're passed along [____].

Animals at [____] [____] as they take in [____] toxin.

 ✓ ✓ 😊 ✓

Dependence on Other Organisms

Ecosystems

ECOSYSTEM —

_____ in an _____
are _____ — they
need _____
(so a _____ in one _____
could easily _____).

E.g. _____ depend on
_____ them.

Humans also _____
_____ — they
_____,
which ensures our _____.

Dependence on Plants

Almost all _____
_____.

Plants use _____
_____.

⬇

They use _____
_____.

⬇

Energy in _____
_____.

Plants produce _____

Plants take in _____

Food Chains

Food chains show _____.

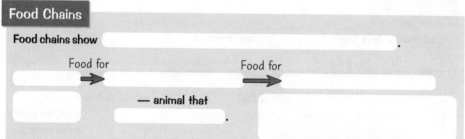

_____ Food for ➡ _____ Food for ➡ _____

_____ — animal that _____.

Food Webs

Food webs show _____

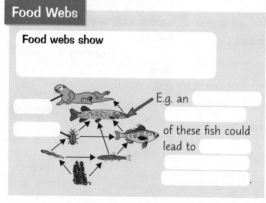

E.g. an _____

of these fish could
lead to _____

_____.

Toxins in Food Chains

Toxins _____

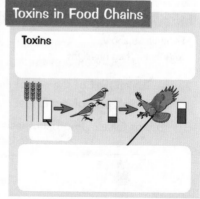

_____

_____.

Mixed Practice Quizzes

That's another section out of the way — with lots of plant-related facts to learn...
Time for some quiz questions to see if your knowledge of p.29-36 has bloomed.

Quiz 1   Date: ...... / ...... / ......

1) Give two ways that pollen can be transferred from one plant to another. ☑

2) What is the food store in a seed used for? ☑

3) Define the term 'ecosystem'. ☑

4) What are the three main parts of a carpel? ☑

5) How do the veins in a leaf help photosynthesis? ☑

6) Describe an experiment you could do to investigate
   how far different types of seeds disperse. ☑

7) State the word equation for photosynthesis. ☑

8) Which part of a flower develops into a fruit? ☑

Total: [   ]

Quiz 2   Date: ...... / ...... / ......

1) Why is chlorophyll needed in photosynthesis? ☑

2) Explain how energy in animals can be linked back to the Sun. ☑

3) Give two things that must be kept the same when
   investigating the effect of wind on seed dispersal. ☑

4) Describe three ways in which leaves are adapted for photosynthesis. ☑

5) Explain why insects are important for ensuring human food supply. ☑

6) Which organisms would you expect to be worst affected by toxins in a
   food chain — ones at the top or ones at the bottom? Explain your answer. ☑

7) a) Which part of the carpel does a pollen tube grow through?
   b) Which part of the carpel does a pollen tube grow towards? ☑

8) True or false? Photosynthesis requires oxygen. ☑

Total: [   ]

Mixed Practice Quizzes

Quiz 3   Date: ...... / ...... / ......

1) Describe how fertilisation occurs in a plant,
   from the point at which pollen lands on the stigma. ☑

2) Explain why all living organisms depend on plants,
   in terms of the gases plants give out and take in. ☑

3) A flower has anthers that are exposed on long filaments.
   Is this plant more likely to be pollinated by insects or the wind? ☑

4) Describe two ways in which seeds can be dispersed by animals. ☑

5) Describe the role of stomata in photosynthesis. ☑

6) Give two substances that a plant's roots absorb from the soil. ☑

7) True or false? The filament is the part of the stamen that
   produces male sex cells. ☑

8) Which two types of organism could be the producer in a food chain? ☑

Total:

Quiz 4   Date: ...... / ...... / ......

1) What term describes an organism in a food chain that eats producers? ☑

2) Explain how seeds are dispersed in the 'drop and roll' method. ☑

3) Describe two ways in which a flower may be adapted for insect pollination. ☑

4) What is a food web? ☑

5) What are the two products of photosynthesis? ☑

6) Define the term 'pollination'. ☑

7) What name is given to the small holes on the underside
   of leaves that are needed for gas exchange? ☑

8) Describe where female sex cells are found in a carpel. ☑

Total:

Section 3 — Plants and Ecosystems

DNA and Inheritance

First Go:
..... /..... /.....

Chromosomes, Genes and DNA

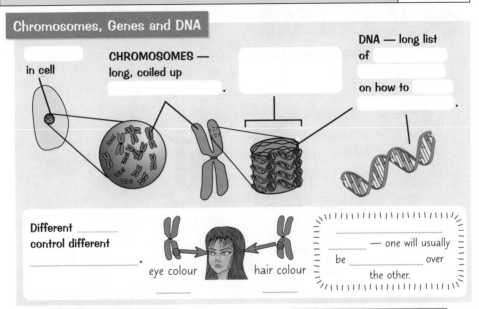

in cell

CHROMOSOMES —
long, coiled up

.

DNA — long list
of

on how to

.

Different ....
control different
.... **.**

eye colour   hair colour

.... — one will usually
be .... over
the other.

Inheriting Characteristics

HEREDITY — ....
....
...........................**.**

In humans, sex cells have ....
.... and body cells have ....

Sex cells contain chromosomes
(.................... that's in body cells)

....

Chromosomes pair up. There's

fertilised egg

Baby inherits
.... and so a
mixture of their characteristics.

The First Model of DNA

....
were the
to build a model of DNA.

....

....

helped them understand that
DNA was a .... **.**

....

(a spiral made of
two chains wound
together)   one chain

 ☑   ☑   ☑

DNA and Inheritance

Chromosomes, Genes and DNA

CHROMOSOMES —

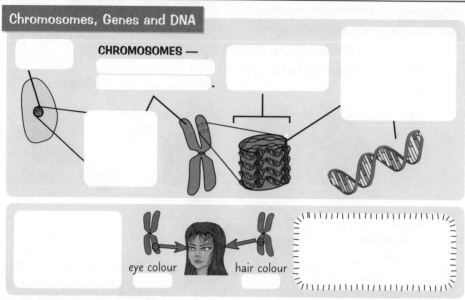

eye colour   hair colour

Inheriting Characteristics

HEREDITY — ....

....

....

In humans, ...

.... and body cells ....

(.......................... that's in body cells)

Chromosomes pair up.

Baby inherits mixture

The First Model of DNA

were the ....
to build ....

one
chain

Section 4 — Inheritance, Variation and Survival

Variation and Natural Selection

Variation

VARIATION — the [_____] all living things.

Variation between [_____] occurs because their [_____] [_____].

Variation [_____] occurs because of:
- [_____] in genes
- [_____]
  (e.g. the [_____] an organism [_____]).
Differences between members of same species (e.g. skin colour) are known as [_____].

Continuous Variation

CONTINUOUS VARIATION — where a [_____] can have [____] value within a [_____], e.g. height or [_____].

E.g.

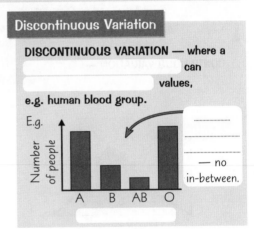

Number of people ↑

Height →

Discontinuous Variation

DISCONTINUOUS VARIATION — where a [_____] can [_____] values, e.g. human blood group.

E.g.

Number of people

A B AB O

....
....
....
— no in-between.

[_____]

Natural Selection

NATURAL SELECTION — the process by which a characteristic gradually becomes ....

Organisms compete for [_____] to survive.

→

Organisms with characteristics that make them [_____] more likely to survive.

→

These organisms [_____] to reproduce and [_____] for useful characteristics to next generation.

They compete with other species and .... of their own species.

Over time, useful [_____]

 ✓   ✓   ✓

Variation and Natural Selection

Variation

VARIATION — [_____].

Variation between	Variation [_____] because of:
	• [_____]
	• [_____]
	Differences between members of

Continuous Variation

CONTINUOUS VARIATION —

E.g.

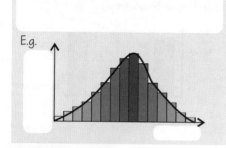

Discontinuous Variation

DISCONTINUOUS VARIATION — where a

E.g.

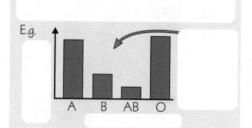

A   B   AB   O

Natural Selection

NATURAL SELECTION — ....
....

	Organisms with characteristics that make	→	These organisms [____] to reproduce and [____] for useful characteristics to next generation.

They compete with other species and ....
....

Section 4 — Inheritance, Variation and Survival

Extinction and Preserving Species

Risk of Extinction

EXTINCTION — when no

_____ of _____ remain.

Species at risk of extinction are called _____ .

Organisms are _____ for competing in their _____ .

⬇

If environment _____ , some organisms may struggle to compete and so _____

_____ .

⬇

If this happens to whole species, _____

Maintaining Biodiversity

BIODIVERSITY — _____

It's important we maintain biodiversity — if a species becomes _____ , it can _____ that rely on that species _____ (including humans).

Important we protect:

- Organisms we _____ for e.g.:
  - Food
  - _____
  - _____

- Organisms we _____ (e.g. deep in ocean) which may be new sources of _____ .

We can protect organisms by e.g. preventing the _____ .

Gene Banks

GENE BANK — a store of the genes of _____ .

If species becomes _____ ➡ ...could use _____ to create _____ of that species.

Gene banks could be a way of maintaining _____ .

In plants:

 ➡ Seeds collected and _____ _____ . ➡ New plants can be _____ .

In animals:

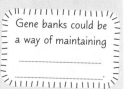 ➡ Sex cells _____ . ➡ Could create new _____ in future.

 ☑ ☑ ☑

| Second Go: |
| ..... /..... /..... |

Extinction and Preserving Species

Risk of Extinction

EXTINCTION —

Species at risk _____
_____ .

Organisms are

⬇

If environment

⬇

Maintaining Biodiversity

BIODIVERSITY —

It's important we maintain biodiversity — if a species

Important we protect:
- Organisms _____ :
  - _____
  - _____
  - _____
- Organisms we

We can protect organisms by e.g. _____
_____ .

Gene Banks

GENE BANK —

If species ➡

In plants:

 ➡ ➡

In animals:

➡ ➡

Section 4 — Inheritance, Variation and Survival

Mixed Practice Quizzes

There's a lot of variation in the questions below... And a lot of DNA, gene banks, and anything else on pages 39-44. Why don't you give them a ~~Crick~~ crack?

Quiz 1 Date: ...... / ...... / ......

1) What is the term given to the process in which a characteristic gradually becomes more (or less) common in a population?

2) True or false? Gene banks could be a way of maintaining biodiversity in the future.

3) What is DNA?

4) Describe why there is variation between different species.

5) Explain why some species could become extinct if their environment changes.

6) How many chromosomes do human sex cells have? What about body cells?

7) Why were Wilkins and Franklin important scientists?

8) Give one way we can protect organisms to help maintain biodiversity.

Total:

Quiz 2 Date: ...... / ...... / ......

1) True or false? DNA is a spiral made of two chains wound together.

2) What are chromosomes?

3) Define heredity.

4) Describe the process of natural selection.

5) Describe the difference between continuous and discontinuous variation.

6) What is a gene bank?

7) In a fertilised egg, how many copies of each gene come from the mother?

8) What does it mean if a species is 'endangered'?

Total:

Section 4 — Inheritance, Variation and Survival

Mixed Practice Quizzes

Quiz 3 Date: ...... / ...... / ......

1) Explain why a baby inherits a mixture of its parents' characteristics.
2) What is a gene?
3) True or false? Organisms only compete for resources with members of their own species.
4) How can gene banks help to protect endangered species?
5) Explain why it's important that we maintain biodiversity.
6) Define variation.
7) What are the names of the scientists who first built a model of DNA?
8) Apart from differences in genes, what else causes characteristic features to arise in a species?

Total:

Quiz 4 Date: ...... / ...... / ......

1) True or false? Continuous variation is where characteristic features can only take certain values.
2) Put the following in order of size, from largest to smallest: gene, nucleus, chromosome.
3) What are characteristic features?
4) Describe how gene banks could be used to:
   a) grow new plants, b) create new animals.
5) What is biodiversity?
6) Give an example of a characteristic in humans that is controlled by genes.
7) Define natural selection.
8) What does it mean if a species is 'extinct'?

Total:

Solids, Liquids and Gases

Solids

Solids, liquids and gases are called
....

particles [＿＿＿] together

This means solids:

• are usually very ....

• are .... easily

....

.... arrangement

particles can't .... ,
but can .... in
....

This means solids:

• have definite ....

• .... volume

• .... flow

The forces of .... between
particles in a solid are ....:

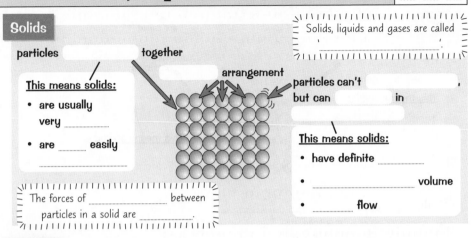

Liquids

particles [＿＿＿] together   [＿＿＿] arrangement   particles move
[＿＿＿] each other

This means liquids:

• are ....

• are not easily
....

This means liquids:

• don't have definite ....

• have definite ....

• flow ....

The forces of ....
between particles in a liquid are ....:

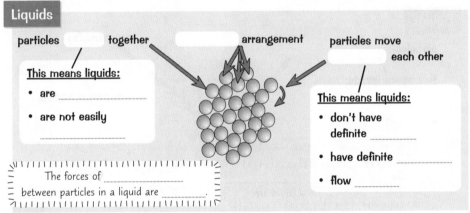

Gases

particles [＿＿＿] [＿＿＿]   arrangement   particles move
in [＿＿＿]

This means gases:

• have a low ....

• ....
compressed

This means gases:

• ....
.... shape

• don't have definite ....

• ....

The forces of .... between
particles in a gas are ....:

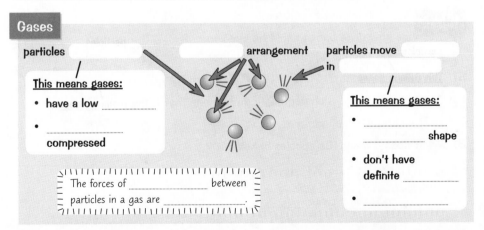

Solids, Liquids and Gases

Solids

_____ are called '_____'

particles

This means solids:

-

-

particles

This means solids:

-

-

-

The _____ of _____ in a solid are _____.

Liquids

particles _____

This means liquids:

-

-

particles

This means liquids:

-

-

-

The _____ of _____ in a liquid are _____.

Gases

particles _____

This means gases:

-

-

particles

This means gases:

-

-

-

The _____ of _____ in a gas are _____.

Section 5 — Classifying Materials

Pressure, Diffusion & Changes of State

Pressure

Gas pressure is caused by _____ hitting a _____.

Two ways to _____ pressure:

1

2

_____

temperature ↓

particles move _____

particles hit _____

and _____ often

pressure _____

_____

volume ↓

particles _____ into _____ space

particles hit _____ often

Diffusion

DIFFUSION — the process of particles _____ from an area of _____ concentration to an _____.

_____ particle

_____ particle

particles _____ slowly _____ a _____ through _____

Particles are _____ by _____ into air particles.

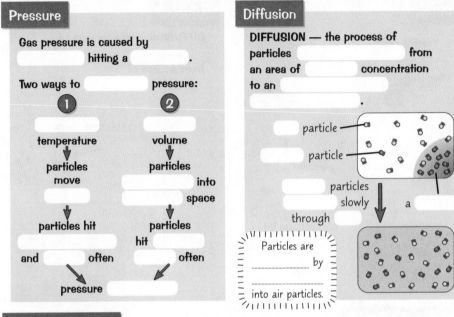

Changes of State

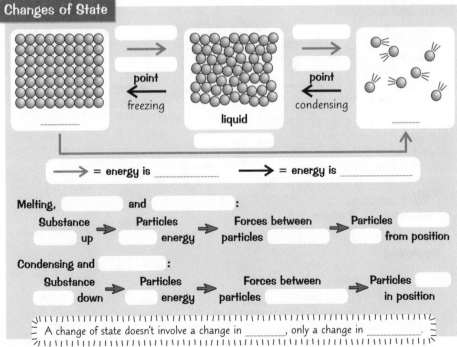

_____

_____ point

freezing ←

....

liquid

_____ point

condensing ←

....

→ = energy is _____   ➡ = energy is _____

Melting, _____ and _____:

Substance _____ up → Particles _____ energy → Forces between particles _____ → Particles _____ from position

Condensing and _____:

Substance _____ down → Particles _____ energy → Forces between particles _____ → Particles _____ in position

A change of state doesn't involve a change in _____, only a change in _____.

 ☑ ☑ ☑

Second Go: ..... / ..... / ..... Pressure, Diffusion & Changes of State

Pressure

Gas pressure

Two ways to

1   2

particles   particles

particles hit   particles hit

Diffusion

DIFFUSION — the process of

from an area of

.

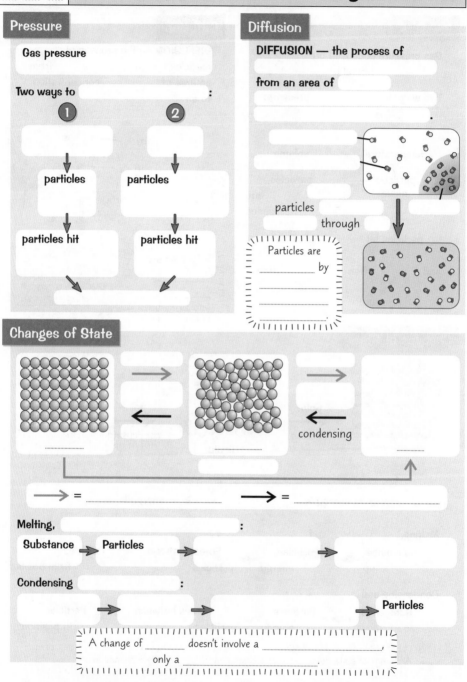

particles

through

Particles are

.... by

....

....

....

Changes of State

condensing

⟶ = ...   ⟶ = ...

Melting,   :

Substance   Particles

Condensing   :

Particles

A change of .... doesn't involve a ....,

only a ....

Atoms, Elements & the Periodic Table

The Dalton Model of the Atom

Atoms are _____ particles that can't be _____.

Dalton (_____) concluded these three things about _____:

1. All _____ is made up of atoms.

2. There are _____ _____ of atom.

3. Each _____ contains a different type of _____.

Elements

ELEMENT — a substance that contains _____ type of _____.

copper   oxygen

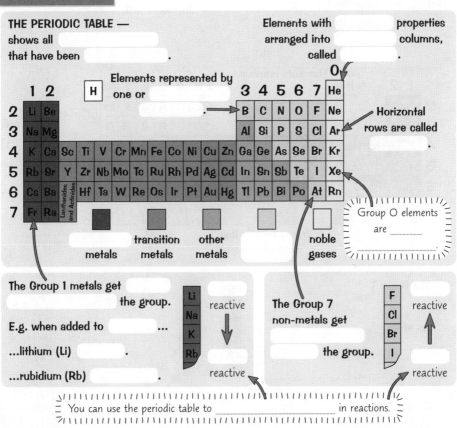

Elements have different _____ E.g. copper is a _____ metal and oxygen is a _____ gas.

The Periodic Table

THE PERIODIC TABLE — shows all _____ that have been _____.

Elements with _____ properties arranged into _____ columns, called _____.

Elements represented by one or _____ _____.

Horizontal rows are called _____.

	1	2	H													3	4	5	6	7	0 He
2	Li	Be															B	C	N	O	F	Ne
3	Na	Mg															Al	Si	P	S	Cl	Ar
4	K	Ca	Sc	Ti	V	Cr	Mn	Fe	Co	Ni	Cu	Zn					Ga	Ge	As	Se	Br	Kr
5	Rb	Sr	Y	Zr	Nb	Mo	Tc	Ru	Rh	Pd	Ag	Cd					In	Sn	Sb	Te	I	Xe
6	Cs	Ba	Lanthanides and Actinides	Hf	Ta	W	Re	Os	Ir	Pt	Au	Hg					Tl	Pb	Bi	Po	At	Rn
7	Fr	Ra																				

_____ metals   transition metals   other metals   _____   noble gases

Group O elements are _____

The Group 1 metals get _____ _____ the group.

E.g. when added to _____ ...

...lithium (Li) _____.

...rubidium (Rb) _____.

Li
Na
K
Rb

reactive ↓ reactive

The Group 7 non-metals get _____ _____ the group.

F
Cl
Br
I

reactive ↑ reactive

You can use the periodic table to _____ in reactions.

Atoms, Elements & the Periodic Table

The Dalton Model of the Atom

Atoms are

Dalton
these three things about _____ :

1 All _____ is made up of _____ .

2 There are

3 Each

Elements

ELEMENT —

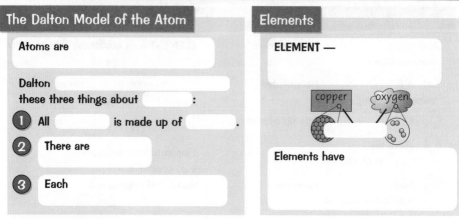

copper   oxygen

Elements have

The Periodic Table

THE PERIODIC TABLE —

Elements with

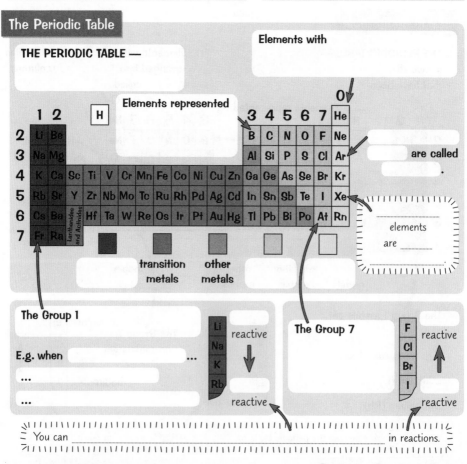

Elements represented

	1	2													3	4	5	6	7	He
			H																	0
2	Li	Be													B	C	N	O	F	Ne
3	Na	Mg													Al	Si	P	S	Cl	Ar
4	K	Ca	Sc	Ti	V	Cr	Mn	Fe	Co	Ni	Cu	Zn	Ga	Ge	As	Se	Br	Kr
5	Rb	Sr	Y	Zr	Nb	Mo	Tc	Ru	Rh	Pd	Ag	Cd	In	Sn	Sb	Te	I	Xe
6	Cs	Ba	Lanthanides and Actinides	Hf	Ta	W	Re	Os	Ir	Pt	Au	Hg	Tl	Pb	Bi	Po	At	Rn
7	Fr	Ra																

_____ are called _____ .

transition metals   other metals

_____ elements are _____

The Group 1

E.g. when _____ ...

...

...

Li
Na
K
Rb

reactive ↓ reactive

The Group 7

F
Cl
Br
I

reactive ↑ reactive

You can _____ in reactions.

Compounds

Molecules and Compounds

If they are atoms of the _____,
then the molecule is _____.
If they are atoms of _____
then the molecule is _____.

MOLECULE — _____
atoms _____.

COMPOUND — a substance made up of _____
from _____ elements, _____.

Molecules in
a _____:

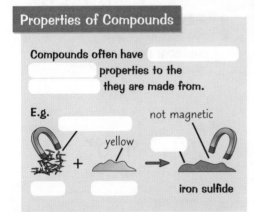

E.g. _____, H_2O

An element made
of _____:

E.g. _____, H_2

An element made
of _____:

E.g. _____, Ar

Properties of Compounds

Compounds often have _____
_____ properties to the
_____ they are made from.

E.g. _____

not magnetic

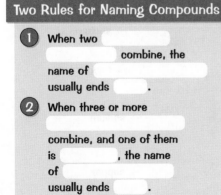

yellow

_____

iron sulfide

Chemical Formulae

CHEMICAL FORMULA — a formula
that shows the _____ of
atoms of _____
in a _____.

E.g. water:

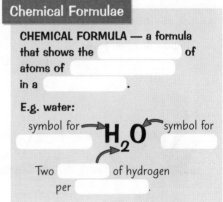

symbol for → H_2O ← symbol for

_____

_____

Two _____ of hydrogen
per _____.

Two Rules for Naming Compounds

1 When two _____
_____ combine, the
name of _____
usually ends _____.

2 When three or more _____
_____
combine, and one of them
is _____, the name
of _____
usually ends _____.

E.g.
_____ → sodium _____
+ chlorine

_____ → magnesium _____
+ oxygen

E.g.
_____ + → sodium _____
carbon + oxygen

_____ + → copper _____
sulfur + oxygen

 ☑ ☑ ☑

54

Compounds

Molecules and Compounds

MOLECULE —

COMPOUND —

If they are _____
_____, then the
_____.
If they are _____
_____, then the
_____.

_____ in
a _____:

An _____ made
of _____:

An _____ made
of _____:

E.g. _____

E.g. _____

E.g. _____

Properties of Compounds

Compounds often have _____
_____ to the
_____.

E.g.

_____ + _____ → _____

_____

Chemical Formulae

CHEMICAL FORMULA — a formula

E.g. _____ :

H_2O

hydrogen _____ .

Two Rules for Naming Compounds

1 When two

E.g.
_____ + _____ → sodium _____

_____ + _____ → magnesium _____

2 When three or more

E.g.
_____ + _____ → sodium _____
+ _____

_____ + _____ → copper _____
+ _____

Mixed Practice Quizzes

Just what you've been waiting for — some terrific quiz questions to test the stuff covered on p.47-54. Don't forget to tot up your totals.

Quiz 1 | Date: ...... / ...... / ......

1) In which state of matter do particles move quickly in all directions?

2) True or false? Hydrogen (H_2) is a compound.

3) State two ways you could increase the pressure of a gas.

4) What are the horizontal rows in the periodic table called?

5) True or false? The compound formed from the reaction between sodium and chlorine is called sodium chlorate.

6) What is the name of the process in which a liquid becomes a gas?

7) What is an element?

8) Give three properties of solids.

Total:

Quiz 2 | Date: ...... / ...... / ......

1) State whether each of the following substances is an element or a compound: a) Water (H_2O), b) Argon (Ar).

2) Which state of matter usually has the highest density?

3) What is the name of the compound made up of copper, sulfur and oxygen?

4) True or false? You can use the periodic table to predict patterns in reactions.

5) Give three things that Dalton concluded about atoms.

6) What is meant by diffusion?

7) What happens to the forces between particles in a solid when the solid is heated?

8) True or false? All elements have similar properties.

Total:

Mixed Practice Quizzes

Quiz 3 Date: ...... / ...... / ......

1) What happens to the pressure of a fixed volume of gas when the gas is heated?

2) True or false? Subliming is when a solid changes into a gas.

3) What is a molecule?

4) What are the vertical columns in the periodic table called?

5) Which states of matter have a definite volume?

6) True or false? The '2' in H_2O tells you that there are two atoms of oxygen in the molecule.

7) Describe the trend in reactivity down Group 7 in the periodic table.

8) Does energy need to be supplied or given out for melting to occur?

Total:

Quiz 4 Date: ...... / ...... / ......

1) True or false? Compounds often have completely different properties to the elements that they're made from.

2) Do Group 1 metals get more or less reactive down the group?

3) What is the name of the compound formed from magnesium and oxygen?

4) True or false? All molecules are compounds.

5) Describe the particle arrangement in a solid.

6) Which state of matter has a definite shape — a solid, a liquid or a gas?

7) Explain, in terms of particles, what happens when a substance condenses.

8) Why do gas particles diffuse slowly through air?

Total:

Purity and Separating Mixtures

Purity

PURE SUBSTANCE — a substance made up of [____] type of [____].

Pure substances have [____] melting and [____].

E.g. pure water boils at [____] and pure ice melts at [____].

You can [____] the purity of a substance by [____].

Pure substances can't be separated into .... without a ....

Mixtures

MIXTURE — a substance made up of [____] elements or [____] that aren't [____] to each other.

E.g. [____] is a mixture.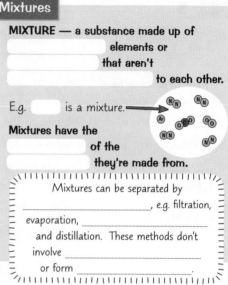

Mixtures have the [____] of the [____] they're made from.

Mixtures can be separated by .... , e.g. filtration, evaporation, ... and distillation. These methods don't involve .... or form ....

Dissolving

SOLUTE — the solid being [____].

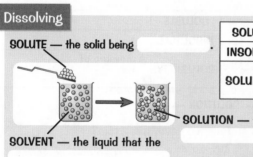

SOLVENT — the liquid that the [____].

SOLUTION — the mixture of [____].

SOLUBLE	.... dissolve
INSOLUBLE	.... dissolve
SOLUBILITY	A measure of how much ....

A solution is called .... when no more .... will ....

Filtration

Separates [____] from liquids — e.g. [____] and water:

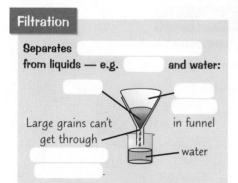

Large grains can't get through

[____] in funnel

water

Evaporation

Separates [____] from liquids — e.g. [____]:

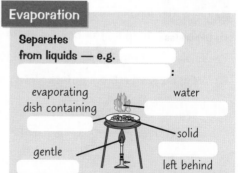

evaporating dish containing [____]

water

gentle [____]

solid

left behind

Section 5 — Classifying Materials

Second Go:
...../...../.....

Purity and Separating Mixtures

Purity

PURE SUBSTANCE — a substance made up of _____ .

Pure substances have _____

E.g. _____ boils at _____ and _____ melts at _____ .

You can _____ of a substance by _____ .

Pure substances can't be _____ .

Mixtures

MIXTURE — _____

E.g. _____ .

Mixtures have the _____

Mixtures can be separated by _____ . These methods don't involve _____

Dissolving

SOLUTE — the solid _____ .

SOLUBLE	
INSOLUBLE	
SOLUBILITY	A measure of

SOLUTION — _____

A solution is _____ when _____ .

SOLVENT — _____

Filtration

Separates _____ — e.g. _____ :

can't get through _____ in funnel

Evaporation

Separates _____ — e.g. _____ :

evaporating dish — water

solid

Section 5 — Classifying Materials

Chromatography and Distillation

Chromatography

Chromatography can [____] in ink —
they [____] paper at [____].

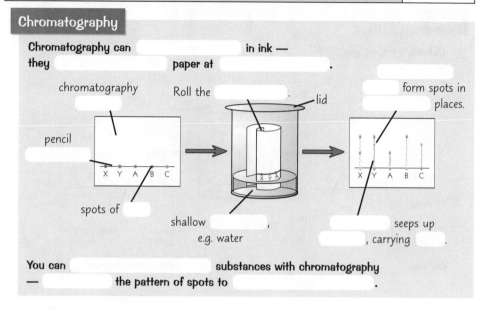

chromatography [____]

Roll the [____].

— lid

[____] form spots in [____] places.

pencil

[____]

spots of [____]

X Y A B C

shallow [____],
e.g. water

X Y A

X Y A B C

[____] seeps up

[____], carrying [____].

You can [____] substances with chromatography
— [____] the pattern of spots to [____].

Two Types of Distillation

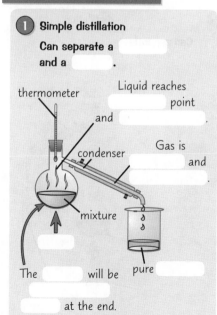

1 Simple distillation

Can separate a [____]
and a [____].

thermometer

Liquid reaches [____] point
and [____].

condenser

Gas is [____]
and [____].

mixture

pure [____]

The [____] will be [____]
at the end.

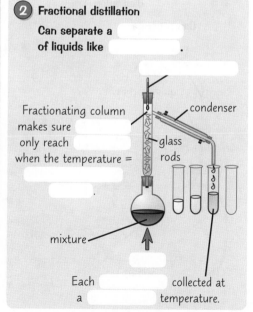

2 Fractional distillation

Can separate a [____]
of liquids like [____].

Fractionating column
makes sure [____]
only reach [____]
when the temperature = [____].

condenser

glass rods

mixture

Each [____] collected at
a [____] temperature.

Chromatography and Distillation

Chromatography

Chromatography can

Roll

form spots in

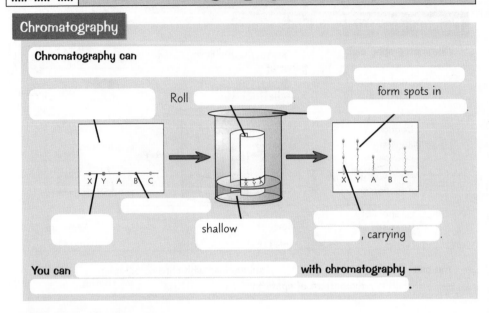

shallow

, carrying

You can _____ **with chromatography —**

Two Types of Distillation

1 _____ **distillation**

Can separate

Liquid reaches

Gas is

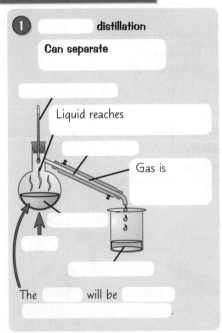

The _____ will be

2 _____ **distillation**

Can separate

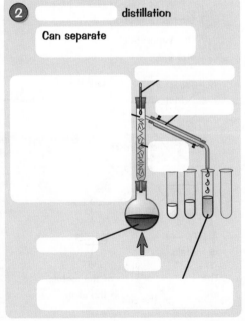

Metals and Non-Metals

Properties of Metals and Non-Metals

	METALS	NON-METALS
Position in the periodic table	....	....
Conduct electricity?	.... electrical conductors	.... electrical conductors
Conduct energy by heating?	.... conductors	.... conductors
Strength	....	.... , easy to ....
Easy to shape?	Yes — .... and ductile	No — .... , will shatter
Density	....	....
Melting and boiling points	....	....
Appearance	Can be	Most are ....
Magnetism	.... are magnetic	Non-magnetic
Sound	Sonorous — make a .... when hit	Not ....

Alloys

ALLOY — a [   ] of metals.

The [   ] of the metals are [   ] in the alloy.

E.g. [   ] is an alloy of [   ] and other elements.

E.g. [   ] is an alloy of [   ] and zinc.

[   ] like iron

[   ] like copper

Metals and Non-Metals

Properties of Metals and Non-Metals

	METALS	NON-METALS
Position in the periodic table		
Conduct electricity?	conductors	conductors
Conduct energy by heating?	conductors	conductors
Strength		, easy to
Easy to shape?	Yes —	No —
Density		
Melting and boiling points		
Appearance	Can be	
Magnetism		
Sound	Sonorous —	Not

Alloys

ALLOY —

The _____ of the _____ are _____ in the _____ .

E.g. _____ is an alloy of _____ .

E.g. _____ is an alloy of _____ .

_____ like iron   _____ like copper

Properties of Other Materials

Polymers, Ceramics and Composites

	Properties	Uses
POLYMERS Made by [____] lots of [____] molecules in long [____]. [____] are examples of [____] polymers.	Poor conductors ([____]) Often [____] Easily moulded Low [____] — good for making things [____] but [____].	[____] helmets [____] casing Carrier [____]
CERAMICS Made by [____] substances to [____]. E.g. pottery is made by [____].	Poor conductors ([____]) Strong [____]	[____] Pottery Glassware
COMPOSITES Made by [____] materials together.	**Concrete** A [____] of [____] and gravel embedded in [____].	High [____] and very [____] — can withstand [____].	[____] materials
	Fibreglass Glass [____] embedded in [____].	Low [____] like [____] but very [____] like [____].	[____] and surfboards

Properties of Other Materials

Polymers, Ceramics and Composites

	Properties	Uses
POLYMERS Made by _____ are examples of _____ _____.	____ conductors (_____) _____ Easily _____ _____ — good for making things _____ .	_____ casing _____
CERAMICS Made by E.g. _____ is made by _____ .	____ conductors (_____) _____ _____	_____ _____ Glassware
Concrete A _____ of _____ and gravel _____ .	_____ and very _____ — can _____ .	
Fibreglass		_____ and surfboards

Mixed Practice Quizzes

Right. Now you've covered the specially-distilled key facts on p.57-64, here's a mixture of questions to test your knowledge. Marvellous.

Quiz 1   Date: ...... / ...... / ......

1) How could you test a substance to see if it is pure? ☑

2) Which substances are typically shiny and sonorous — metals or non-metals? ☑

3) True or false? Polymers and ceramics are insulators. ☑

4) Why can a mixture of dyes be separated by chromatography? ☑

5) What is the purpose of the fractionating column in fractional distillation? ☑

6) True or false? Mixtures can be separated using physical methods. ☑

7) Which substances generally have a higher density — metals or non-metals? ☑

8) Give an example of an alloy. ☑

Total:

Quiz 2   Date: ...... / ...... / ......

1) Define the term 'solvent'. ☑

2) What is left in the flask after simple distillation? ☑

3) What type of material is pottery — a ceramic or a composite? ☑

4) What is a saturated solution? ☑

5) True or false? A mixture containing a soluble solid and a liquid can be separated by evaporation. ☑

6) Provide two examples of everyday objects made from polymers. ☑

7) Give one method you could use to separate a sand and water mixture. ☑

8) Which substances are good electrical conductors — metals or non-metals? ☑

Total:

Section 5 — Classifying Materials

Mixed Practice Quizzes

Quiz 3 Date: ...... / ...... / ......

1) What is fibreglass — a polymer, a ceramic or a composite?

2) True or false? Fractional distillation can be used to separate a mixture of liquids.

3) Name a composite that can be used as a building material.

4) True or false? A substance containing only one type of compound is a pure substance.

5) What does it mean if a compound is 'insoluble'?

6) Give two properties of polymers.

7) Give an example of a mixture that can be separated by chromatography.

8) True or false? Non-metals are generally malleable and ductile.

Total:

Quiz 4 Date: ...... / ...... / ......

1) Define the term 'alloy'.

2) Which substances would you expect to be brittle and act as electrical insulators — metals or non-metals?

3) Give two properties of fibreglass.

4) True or false? The parts of a mixture are chemically bonded to each other.

5) Define the term 'solubility'.

6) What name is given to the composite that's made from sand and gravel embedded in cement?

7) How can chromatography be used to identify unknown substances?

8) Which substances typically have high melting and boiling points — metals or non-metals?

Total:

Chemical Reactions and Equations

First Go:
..... /..... /.....

Chemical Reactions

Atoms are _____ during a chemical reaction.

The _____ between the reactant atoms are _____, and new _____ are _____.

A change in _____ or a _____ in the reaction mixture (e.g. a _____) can tell you a reaction has _____.

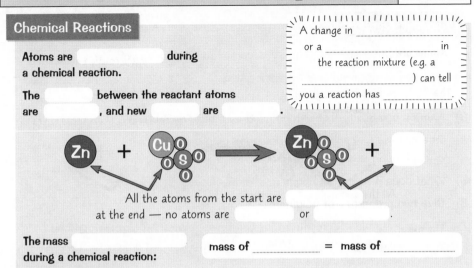

All the atoms from the start are _____ at the end — no atoms are _____ or _____.

The mass _____ during a chemical reaction:

mass of _____ = mass of _____

Word Equations

WORD EQUATION — an equation that expresses a _____

using the _____ of the _____ involved.

carbon + oxygen ⟶ _____

Reactants — the chemicals you _____

Products — the chemicals you _____

Symbol Equations

SYMBOL EQUATION — an equation that expresses a _____ using chemical _____ and _____.

Symbol equations must be _____ (have _____ of atoms of each element on _____).

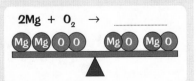

$$2Mg + O_2 \rightarrow \text{_____}$$

Catalysts

CATALYST — a substance which speeds up a _____, without being _____ or used up in the _____.

This means catalysts can be _____.

Catalysts _____ the minimum amount of _____ needed for _____.

This means the reaction can be _____ at a _____.

Second Go: ...../...../..... Chemical Reactions and Equations

Chemical Reactions

Atoms are

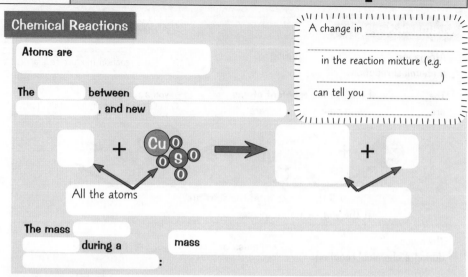

A change in _____

in the reaction mixture (e.g. _____)

can tell you _____

The _____ **between** _____
_____ **, and new** _____ .

All the atoms

The mass _____
_____ **during a** _____ **mass**
_____ :

Word Equations

WORD EQUATION —
an equation that _____
_____
_____

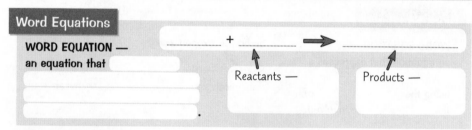

Reactants —

Products —

Symbol Equations

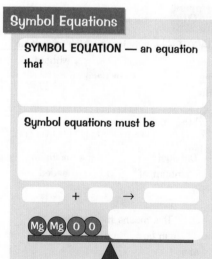

SYMBOL EQUATION — an equation that _____

Symbol equations must be _____

Catalysts

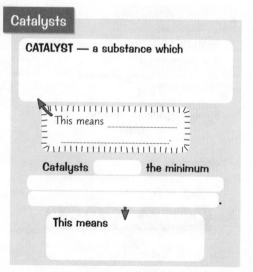

CATALYST — a substance which _____

This means _____

Catalysts _____ **the minimum**
_____ .

This means _____

Examples of Chemical Reactions

Exothermic and Endothermic Reactions

All reactions involve a .... in energy.
The energy is usually ....

EXOTHERMIC reaction:

.... energy to the

.... — shown by a .... in temperature.

Reactions include: ....

Uses include: ....

ENDOTHERMIC reaction:

.... energy from the

.... — shown by a .... in temperature.

Reactions include: ....

Uses include: Some sports ....

Oxidation

OXIDATION — when a substance ....

Oxidation reactions include:

- ....
- .... of iron

iron + ... ⟹ iron oxide (............)

Thermal Decomposition

THERMAL DECOMPOSITION — when a substance .... into at least .... when ....

The substance doesn't .... with anything, but it's still a ....

Some metal .... break down .... to form a metal oxide and ....

Combustion

COMBUSTION (............) — when a .... reacts with .... and releases ....

The .... is transferred by .... and ....

Combustion needs:
- ....
- heat
- ....

Hydrocarbons are often used as .... :

hydrocarbon + ... ⟹ .... + ...

Examples of Chemical Reactions

Exothermic and Endothermic Reactions

All reactions involve ....
The .... is usually ....

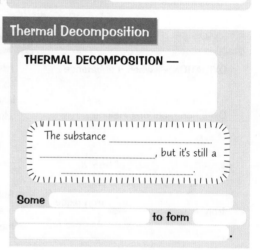

.... reaction:

.... — shown
by a ....

Reactions include: ....
Uses include: ....

.... reaction:

.... — shown by a ....

Reactions include: ....
Uses include: Some ....

Oxidation

OXIDATION —

Oxidation .... include:

• ....

• ....

.... + ⟶ ....
.... (...............)

Thermal Decomposition

THERMAL DECOMPOSITION —

The substance ....
..................................., but it's still a
....

Some ....

.... to form ....
....

Combustion

COMBUSTION ....

.... is transferred by ....

Combustion needs:

• .... • .... • ....

.... are often used as .... :

.... + ... ⟹ .... + ...

Acids, Alkalis and Making Salts

The pH Scale

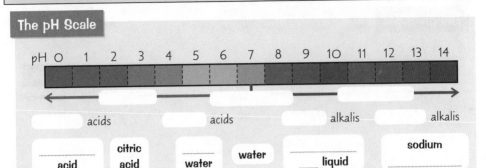

pH 0 1 2 3 4 5 6 7 8 9 10 11 12 13 14

|_____ acids | _____ acids | _____ alkalis | _____ alkalis |

| _____ acid | citric acid | _____ water | water | _____ liquid | sodium _____ |

Neutralisation Reactions

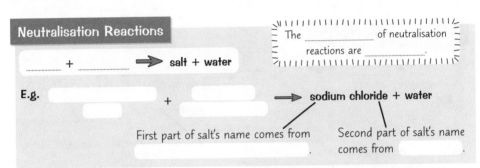

_____ + _____ ⟹ salt + water

The _____ of neutralisation reactions are _____.

E.g. _____ + _____ ⟹ sodium chloride + water

First part of salt's name comes from _____.

Second part of salt's name comes from _____.

Two Types of Indicator

INDICATOR — something that changes _____ depending on whether it's in _____.

1 Litmus Paper

Acids turn _____.

Alkalis turn _____.

2 Universal indicator — gives the _____ of colours shown on _____.

Four Steps for Making Salts

1 acid — alkali —

Add acid to alkali _____.

2 _____ glass rod paper

_____

Check every few _____.

3 _____ dish

When _____, boil off most of the _____.

4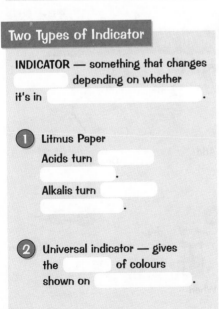

Leave solution to _____.

 ☑ ☑ ☑

Acids, Alkalis and Making Salts

The pH Scale

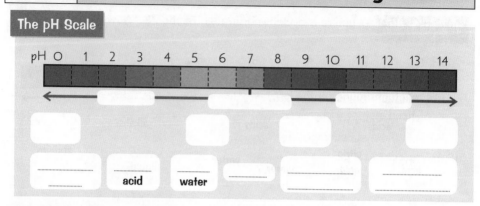

pH 0   1   2   3   4   5   6   7   8   9   10   11   12   13   14

acid   water

Neutralisation Reactions

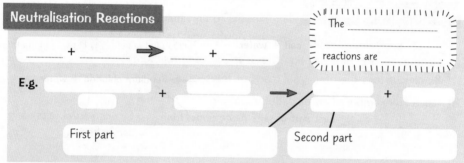

_____ + _____ ➡ _____ + _____

The _____

_____ reactions are _____ .

E.g. _____ + _____ ➡ _____ + _____

First part   Second part

Two Types of Indicator

INDICATOR —

1 Litmus Paper

2 Universal indicator —

Four Steps for Making Salts

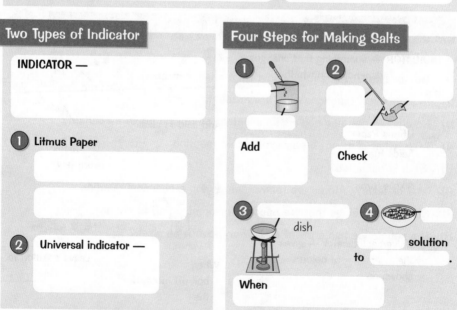

1   **2**

Add   Check

3 _____ dish   **4** _____

When   _____ solution

to _____ .

Mixed Practice Quizzes

Well look at that — you're over halfway through Section 6. Now catalyse your learning of p.67-72 with these quick questions. Easy-peasy citric acid squeezy.

Quiz 1 Date: ...... / ...... / ......

1) Are reactants found on the left-hand side or the right-hand side of a chemical equation?

2) What is thermal decomposition?

3) Give the pH of a neutral substance.

4) What is a catalyst?

5) Give the word equation for a neutralisation reaction.

6) When making a salt by adding an acid to an alkali, at what point should you stop adding the acid?

7) True or false? In a reaction, the total mass of reactants is always less than the total mass of the products.

8) Give an example of an oxidation reaction.

Total:

Quiz 2 Date: ...... / ...... / ......

1) True or false? All reactions involve a change in energy.

2) In a chemical reaction, what are products?

3) How could you use universal indicator to find the pH of a solution?

4) State what is meant by an exothermic reaction.

5) What is oxidation?

6) True or false? Atoms are rearranged during a chemical reaction.

7) Name three things that are needed for combustion to occur.

8) If a substance has a pH of 6, is it an acid or an alkali?

Total:

Mixed Practice Quizzes

Quiz 3   Date: ...... / ...... / ......

1) What happens during a combustion reaction?

2) Why can catalysts be reused?

3) What is a symbol equation?

4) Give one way of telling that a chemical reaction has occurred.

5) What name is given to a substance that changes colour depending on whether it is in an acid or an alkali?

6) What type of reaction is the rusting of iron?

7) State two ways in which the energy released by combustion reactions is transferred to the surroundings.

8) True or false? Catalysts work by raising the minimum temperature needed for a reaction to happen.

Total:

Quiz 4   Date: ...... / ...... / ......

1) True or false? Atoms are destroyed and recreated during chemical reactions.

2) What happens to the temperature of the surroundings during an endothermic reaction?

3) What would you call a substance with a pH of 9: a weak acid, a strong acid, a weak alkali or a strong alkali?

4) What colour do alkalis turn litmus paper?

5) How many reactants are there in a thermal decomposition reaction?

6) What does it mean if a symbol equation is balanced?

7) What type of chemical equation uses the full names of the chemicals involved?

8) Describe the steps you would take to make salt crystals from an acid and an alkali.

Total:

Reactivity of Metals

The Reactivity Series

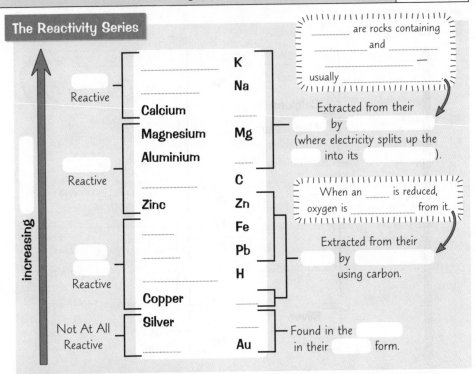

increasing

.... Reactive

K
Na
....
Calcium
Magnesium   Mg
Aluminium   ....

.... Reactive

C
Zn

Zinc

Fe
Pb

.... Reactive

H

Copper
Silver

Au

Not At All Reactive

.... are rocks containing
.... and ....
.... — ....
usually ....

Extracted from their .... by ....
(where electricity splits up the .... into its ....).

When an .... is reduced, oxygen is .... from it.

Extracted from their .... by .... using carbon.

Found in the .... in their .... form.

Reactions of Metals with Acids

Needs to be above .... in the .... series.

metal + acid ➡️ .... + ...

Test for .... using a ....

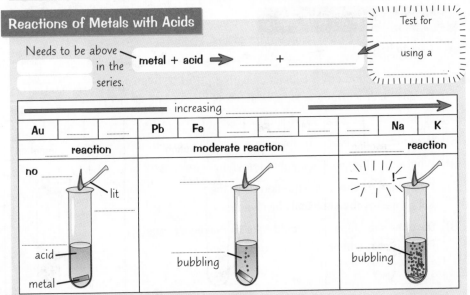

increasing									
Au	......	......	Pb	Fe	......	......	......	Na	K
.... reaction			moderate reaction				.... reaction		

no ....

.... lit

....

.... acid

metal

....

bubbling

!

bubbling

 ✓ ✓ ✓

Section 6 — Chemical Changes

Second Go:
...../...../.....

Reactivity of Metals

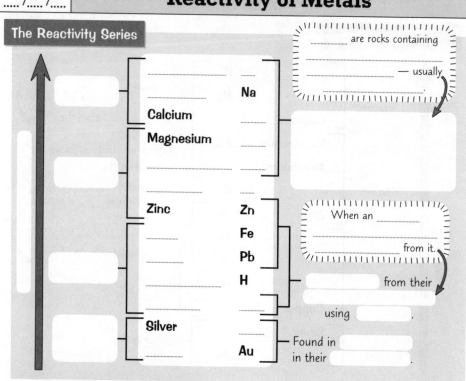

The Reactivity Series

.... are rocks containing

.... — usually

....

....

Na

Calcium

Magnesium

When an ....

.... from it.

Zinc

Zn

Fe

Pb

H

.... from their

using ....

....

Silver

Found in ....
in their

Au

Reactions of Metals with Acids

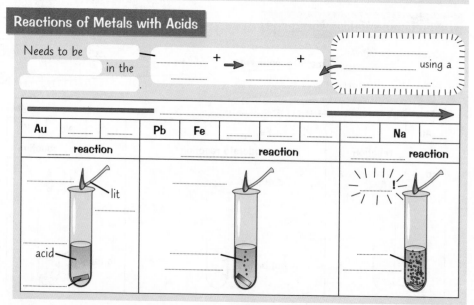

Needs to be ....

.... in the

....

+   →   ....   +

.... using a

....

Au	....	....	Pb	Fe	....	....	....	Na	....
.... reaction			.... reaction				.... reaction		

lit

....

....

acid

....

!

....

Oxides and Displacement Reactions

First Go: ..... /..... /.....

Metal and Non-Metal Oxides

	METAL OXIDES		NON-METAL OXIDES	
Formation:	metal + [____] → metal oxide		non-metal + [____] →	non-metal oxide
pH:	higher than 7 ([____])		lower than 7 ([____])	
Reactivity:	Will react with [____]:		Will react with [____]:	
	[____] + metal oxide → salt + [____]		[____] + non-metal oxide → [____] + water	

Displacement Reactions

DISPLACEMENT REACTION — when a [____] element displaces a [____] element from its [____].

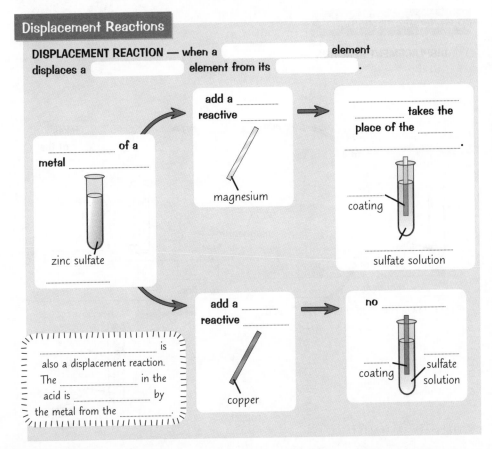

.... of a metal [____]

zinc sulfate

add a [____] reactive [____]

magnesium

.... takes the place of the ....

.... coating

.... sulfate solution

add a [____] reactive [____]

copper

no ....

.... coating .... sulfate solution

.... is also a displacement reaction. The .... in the acid is .... by the metal from the ....

Second Go: ..... /..... /..... Oxides and Displacement Reactions

Metal and Non-Metal Oxides

	OXIDES	OXIDES
Formation:		
pH:	_____ than 7 (_____)	_____ than 7 (_____)
Reactivity:	Will react with _____ :	Will react with _____ :

Displacement Reactions

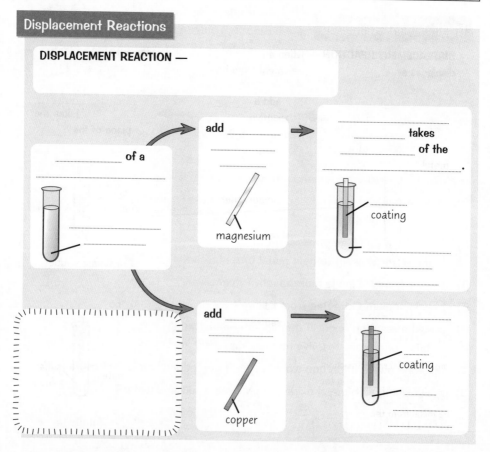

DISPLACEMENT REACTION —

_____ of a

_____ of a

add _____

magnesium

_____ takes _____ of the _____ .

coating

add _____

copper

coating

Mixed Practice Quizzes

Okay, don't react violently — it's time for some more super-quick questions just to check everything from p.75-78 has sunk in. Best of luck.

Quiz 1   Date: ...... / ...... / ......

1) True or false? Most metal oxides are acidic.

2) Which of the following metals is the most reactive: iron, calcium or gold?

3) What happens during a displacement reaction?

4) True or false? A metal above hydrogen in the reactivity series will react with dilute acids.

5) Name two metals that can be extracted from their ores by reduction with carbon.

6) What would you expect to happen if you added a strip of magnesium to a test tube containing zinc sulfate solution?

7) What is produced when a non-metal oxide is added to an alkali?

8) Name an element which is found in the earth in its pure form.

Total:

Quiz 2   Date: ...... / ...... / ......

1) Give a general word equation for the formation of metal oxides.

2) What gas would be produced in the reaction between a metal and dilute acid?

3) An oxide of an element has a pH of 9. Is the element likely to be a metal or a non-metal?

4) True or false? Zinc is more reactive than silver.

5) How is sodium extracted from its ore?

6) Would a reaction occur if you added a metal to a solution of a more-reactive metal compound?

7) Give one observation you would make if you added calcium to dilute acid.

8) What reacts with metal oxides to produce a salt and water?

Total:

Section 6 — Chemical Changes

Mixed Practice Quizzes

Quiz 3   Date: ...... / ...... / ......

1) How can you test whether gas in a test tube is hydrogen?
   Say what you would do and what you would observe.

2) True or false? Iron reacts violently with dilute acid.

3) What is an ore?

4) Will copper displace zinc from a solution of zinc sulfate?

5) State which of the following metals is less reactive than hydrogen:
   aluminium, copper, lead, zinc.

6) The reaction between a reactive metal and dilute acid produces
   a gas and one other product. What is the other product?

7) True or false? Neutralisation is a displacement reaction.

8) Will gold react with dilute acid?

Total:

Quiz 4   Date: ...... / ...... / ......

1) Name three metals that are extracted from their ores by electrolysis.

2) Name one metal that will react violently with dilute acid.

3) A lit splint is held to a test tube of gas and a squeaky pop is heard.
   What gas was in the test tube?

4) Describe the pH of non-metal oxides.

5) What would you observe if you added a small piece of lead to dilute acid?

6) Put the following three metals in order of reactivity, from least reactive
   to most reactive: sodium, iron, magnesium.

7) True or false? Metal oxides will react with acids.

8) When a piece of metal is left in a zinc sulfate solution, a coating of
   zinc forms on the metal. Is the metal more or less reactive than zinc?

Total:

The Earth's Structure

First Go:
..... / ..... / .....

The Earth's Layers

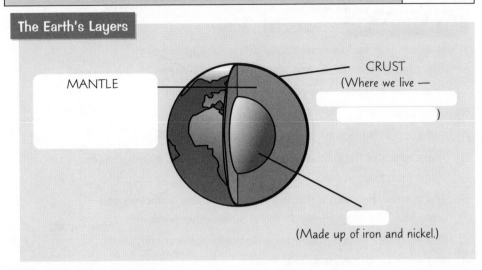

MANTLE

CRUST
(Where we live —

)

(Made up of iron and nickel.)

Composition of Rocks

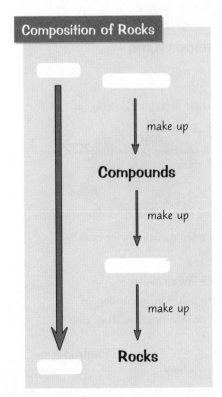

make up

Compounds

make up

make up

Rocks

Tectonic Plates

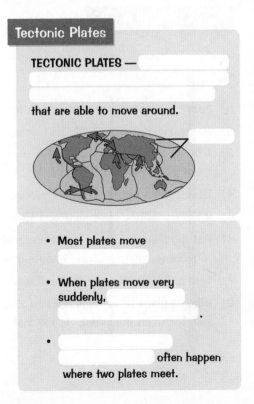

TECTONIC PLATES —

that are able to move around.

- Most plates move

- When plates move very suddenly,
  .

- often happen
  where two plates meet.

The Earth's Structure

The Earth's Layers

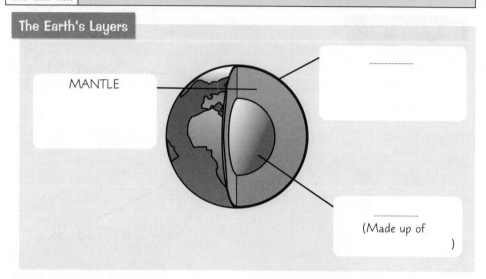

MANTLE

....

....
(Made up of
)

Composition of Rocks

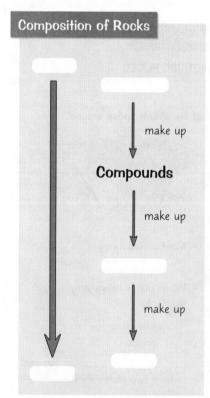

make up

Compounds

make up

make up

Tectonic Plates

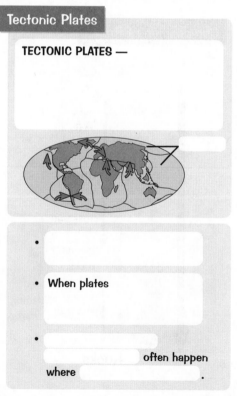

TECTONIC PLATES —

-
- **When plates**
-

                    often happen
where   .

Section 7 — The Earth and The Atmosphere

Rocks

Three Types of Rock

Type of rock	Formed when...	Examples
1 Igneous (Minerals randomly arranged in _____ .)	_____ is pushed up to the Earth's surface (often through volcanoes) _____ . **EXTRUSIVE** — cooled quickly above ground. **INTRUSIVE** — cooled slowly _____ .	_____ (extrusive) Granite _____
2 _____ (Layers of sediment cemented together by _____ .)	Layers of sediment laid down in lakes/ seas over _____ . These rocks often contain _____ .	_____ _____
3 _____ (May contain layers or tiny crystals.)		Marble _____ Schist

The Rock Cycle

The rock cycle takes _____ to complete.

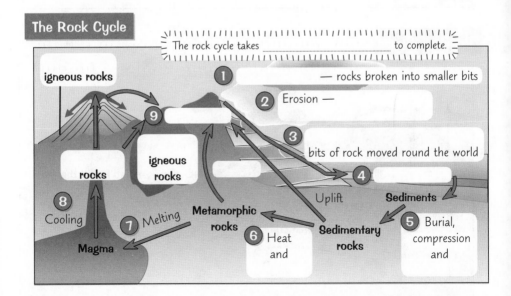

igneous rocks

1 _____ — rocks broken into smaller bits

2 Erosion —

3 _____ bits of rock moved round the world

9

igneous rocks

4 _____

rocks

8 Cooling

7 Melting

Metamorphic rocks

6 Heat and

Uplift

Sediments

Sedimentary rocks

5 Burial, compression and

Magma

Section 7 — The Earth and The Atmosphere

Rocks

Three Types of Rock

Type of rock	Formed when...	Examples
1 Igneous (Minerals	EXTRUSIVE — cooled quickly above ground INTRUSIVE —	....
2 .... (Layers of sediment	Layers of sediment	....
3 .... (May contain layers or tiny		Marble ....

The Rock Cycle

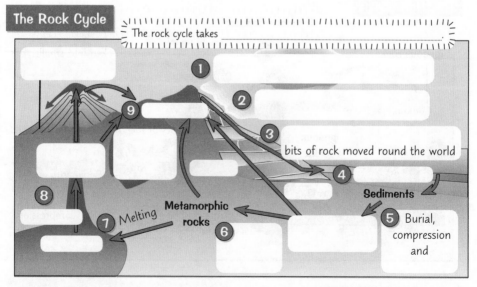

The rock cycle takes ....

bits of rock moved round the world

Sediments

5 Burial, compression and

7 Melting

Metamorphic rocks

Section 7 — The Earth and The Atmosphere

Recycling and the Carbon Cycle

Resources

The Earth is _____
_____.

Metals come from _____
_____ in the Earth's crust.

Some of our energy comes from
_____ (coal, crude oil
and _____).

_____ is also used
to make plastics.

These resources are limited — once
they're used up, we can't _____
_____
_____.

Recycling

RECYCLING — _____
_____ and using
the materials _____.

Four reasons why recycling is
better than _____
_____ :

1. Uses less of the Earth's
_____.

2. _____

3. ...which also saves _____.

4. _____

It's generally more efficient _____
_____

to recycle materials than to throw them
away and _____.

_____. E.g. the energy saving for recycling
aluminium is 95%, but for plastic it's only 70%.

The Carbon Cycle

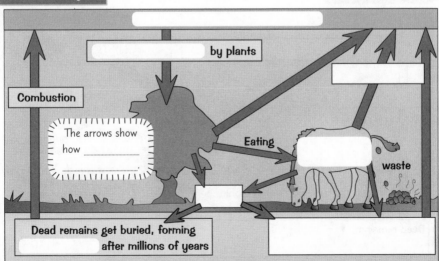

_____

_____ by plants

Combustion

The arrows show
how _____

Eating

_____

waste

Dead remains get buried, forming
_____ after millions of years

 ☑ ☑ ☑

Second Go:
..... /..... /.....

Recycling and the Carbon Cycle

Resources

The Earth is _____ .

Metals come from _____

_____

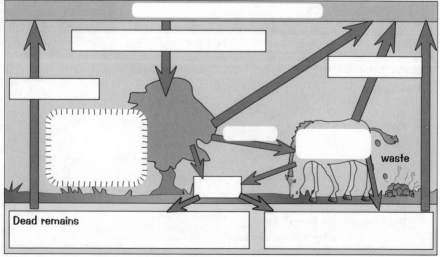

These resources are limited — once

_____

_____ .

Recycling

RECYCLING — _____

_____

_____ .

Four reasons why recycling is better than

_____ :

1 _____

2 _____

3 ...which also saves _____ .

4 _____

It's generally more efficient

_____ . E.g. the energy saving for recycling
aluminium is 95%, but for plastic it's only 70%.

The Carbon Cycle

waste

Dead remains

The Atmosphere and Climate

Composition of the Atmosphere

oxygen (O$_2$)

0.04% carbon dioxide ( )
+
amounts of other gases, e.g.

and noble gases

There's actually .... in the Earth's atmosphere.

78%

Carbon Dioxide in the Atmosphere

Two _____ that increase carbon dioxide levels:

1 _____ to power cars and make electricity.

2 _____ — fewer trees means _____ _____ by photosynthesis.

Global Warming

(such as carbon dioxide)

Energy trapped by greenhouse gases.

from the Sun

GLOBAL WARMING —

Most scientists believe that global warming is due to increasing amounts of carbon dioxide —

Two possible effects of global warming :

1 .... and ice sheets melt → Sea levels .... → ....

2 .... change → Harder to grow ....

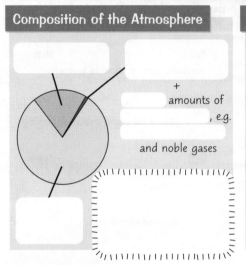

88

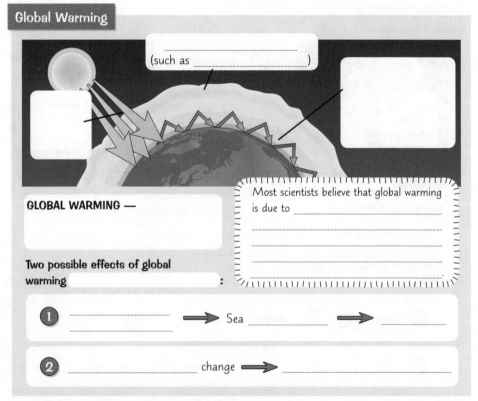

The Atmosphere and Climate

Composition of the Atmosphere

+
amounts of
, e.g.

and noble gases

Carbon Dioxide in the Atmosphere

Two _____ that
increase _____ :

①

②

by photosynthesis.

Global Warming

_____
(such as _____)

GLOBAL WARMING —

Most scientists believe that global warming
is due to _____
_____
_____
_____

**Two possible effects of global
warming** _____ :

① _____ ⟶ Sea _____ ⟶ _____

② _____ change ⟶ _____

Section 7 — The Earth and The Atmosphere

Mixed Practice Quizzes

Get ready to recycle your knowledge of p.81-88 for the quizzes below.
Believe me, there are some questions here that will rock your world...

Quiz 1 Date: ...... / ...... / ......

1) True or false? It is generally more efficient to recycle materials than to throw them away and produce new ones.
2) Describe how sedimentary rocks are formed.
3) What is meant by global warming?
4) Put the following in order of size: minerals, elements, rocks, compounds.
5) What is the thin, solid outer layer of the Earth called?
6) State one use for fossil fuels.
7) True or false? The rock cycle takes millions of years to complete.
8) Describe one human activity that increases the amount of carbon dioxide in the Earth's atmosphere.

Total:

Quiz 2 Date: ...... / ...... / ......

1) True or false? Minerals are made up of rocks.
2) Name the two processes that return carbon dioxide to the air in the carbon cycle.
3) Explain why deforestation increases the level of carbon dioxide in the atmosphere.
4) What type of rock is formed by magma from the Earth's mantle being pushed up to the surface and cooling?
5) Marble is an example of which type of rock?
6) What is the Earth's core made up of?
7) True or false? Earthquakes can happen when tectonic plates move very suddenly.
8) Explain how global warming may lead to flooding.

Total:

Mixed Practice Quizzes

Quiz 3   Date: ...... / ...... / ......

1) Which type of rock may contain either layers or tiny crystals? ☑

2) Describe two ways that carbon in dead animals can be returned to the air. ☑

3) Put these layers in order from the centre of the Earth outwards:
   mantle, core, crust. ☑

4) What happens during the 'transportation' stage of the rock cycle? ☑

5) What are tectonic plates? ☑

6) True or false? Carbon dioxide makes up a
   large percentage of the Earth's atmosphere. ☑

7) True or false? Heat and pressure turns
   metamorphic rocks into sedimentary rocks. ☑

8) What is meant by recycling? ☑

Total:

Quiz 4   Date: ...... / ...... / ......

1) Describe the difference between extrusive and intrusive igneous rocks. ☑

2) Name the process that removes carbon dioxide
   from the air in the carbon cycle. ☑

3) True or false? All of the Earth's resources are unlimited. ☑

4) Which two stages of the rock cycle occur
   between weathering and deposition? ☑

5) Explain how greenhouse gases keep the Earth warm. ☑

6) What percentage of the Earth's atmosphere is: a) nitrogen,   b) oxygen? ☑

7) True or false? Volcanoes are usually found in
   places where two tectonic plates meet. ☑

8) State three reasons why recycling is better
   than making new things from scratch. ☑

Total:

Section 7 — The Earth and The Atmosphere

Energy Stores and Transfer

First Go:
..... /..... /.....

Seven Types of Energy Store

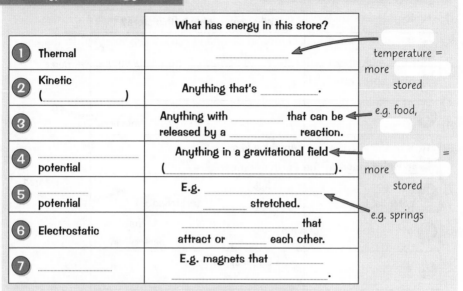

		What has energy in this store?
1	Thermal	....
2	Kinetic (...............)	Anything that's ....
3	....	Anything with .... that can be released by a .... reaction.
4	.... potential	Anything in a gravitational field (...............................).
5	.... potential	E.g. .... stretched.
6	Electrostatic	.... that attract or .... each other.
7	....	E.g. magnets that ....

temperature = more .... stored

e.g. food,

.... = more .... stored

e.g. springs

Five Examples of Energy Transfer Between Stores

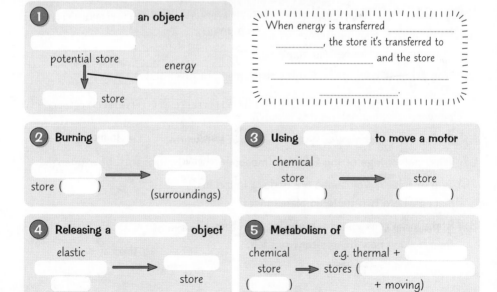

1 .... an object

....

potential store

energy

.... store

When energy is transferred ...., the store it's transferred to .... and the store ....

2 Burning ....

.... store ( ) → .... (surroundings)

3 Using .... to move a motor

chemical store ( ) → .... store ( )

4 Releasing a .... object

elastic .... → .... store

5 Metabolism of ....

chemical store ( ) → e.g. thermal + ... stores (............. + moving)

Energy Stores and Transfer

Seven Types of Energy Store

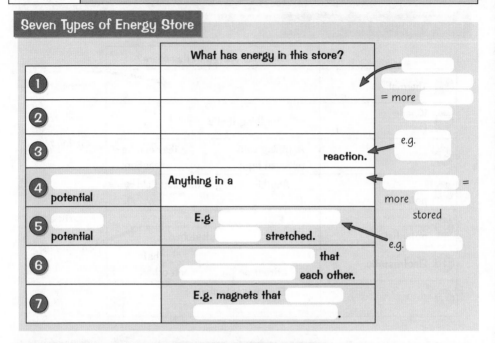

		What has energy in this store?	
1			
2			= more
3		reaction.	e.g.
4	potential	Anything in a	= more stored
5	potential	E.g. stretched.	e.g.
6		that each other.	
7		E.g. magnets that .	

Five Examples of Energy Transfer Between Stores

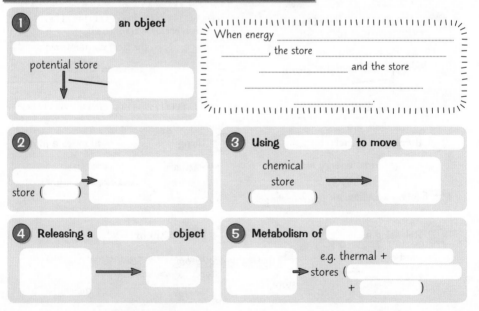

1 an object

potential store

When energy ...., the store .... and the store ....

2

store ( ) →

3 Using to move

chemical store ( ) →

4 Releasing a object →

5 Metabolism of

e.g. thermal + → stores (+)

Energy Transfer

Four Ways of Transferring Energy

1 Mechanically — a force _____
_____ .

e.g. _____ , pulling,
_____ , squeezing

2 Electrically —
_____
move around _____ .

3 Heating — _____
_____ objects transfer
energy to _____ .

4 Light and sound —
_____ transfer energy
_____ .

Moving Objects

When _____ moves an object
_____ ,
energy is _____ to the
_____ kinetic energy store:

energy transferred / work done (_____)

$$= F \times d \text{——} \underline{} \text{ moved}$$

_____ (newtons, N) (_____)

Provider of force (e.g. _____)
needs a _____
to move the object.

A machine that can _____ _____ of energy can either:	
Apply a _____ force...	...over shorter _____ .
or	
Apply a _____ _____ ...	... _____ distance.

Two Principles of Energy

1 **CONSERVATION OF ENERGY** — _____ created
or destroyed, only _____ .

2 Energy is only useful _____ between stores.

Real Energy Transfers

Energy transfers are _____ — some energy will always
_____ (usually by _____).

total energy input = _____ energy + _____ energy

E.g. heating a saucepan:

_____

energy store
of _____

thermal energy
store _____
— _____ energy

thermal energy store _____
— _____ energy

If you know how
much energy _____
_____
and how much _____
_____ , you can
calculate _____
_____ .

Energy Transfer

Four Ways of Transferring Energy

1. **Mechanically —**

   e.g. _____ , pulling,
   _____ , squeezing

2.

3.

4. **Light and sound —**

Moving Objects

kinetic energy store:

energy transferred / work done (_____)

/

/

Provider of force (e.g. _____ **)**
needs a _____ .

_____ **that can** _____ **of energy can either:**	
Apply _____ ... _____ ...	...
or	... _____
...	**distance.**

Two Principles of Energy

1. **CONSERVATION OF ENERGY —**

2.

Real Energy Transfers

Energy transfers _____ **— some energy** _____
_____ .

total _____ **=** _____ **+** _____

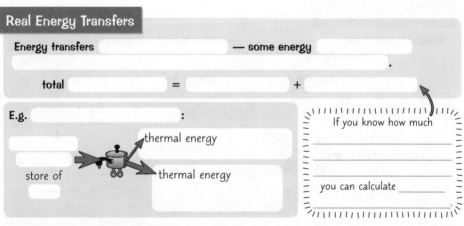

E.g. _____ :

thermal energy

store of

thermal energy

If you know how much
....
....
you can calculate _____

Heating

Thermal Equilibrium

Hotter objects [_____] [_____] by heating.

→ The hotter object [_____] and the cooler object [_____].

→ Energy transfer continues until [_____].

THERMAL EQUILIBRIUM — the point [_____] have the same [_____].

[_____] are two methods of heating.

Conduction

CONDUCTION — process where [_____] particles transfer [_____] to [_____].

Particles in [_____] vibrate faster and [_____] when they bump into [_____] particles.

The objects must [_____].

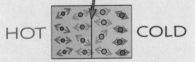

HOT [____] COLD

—— Energy transfer ⟹

Radiation

RADIATION — process where objects [_____] that transfer energy to [_____].

The hotter the object is, the [_____]

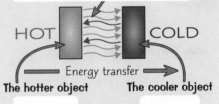

HOT [____] COLD

← Energy transfer →

The hotter object [_____] than it absorbs, so it [_____].

The cooler object [_____] than it radiates, so it [_____].

The objects don't [_____].

Insulators

INSULATOR — a material that [_____] much more [_____].

Insulating an object [_____] energy transfer [_____]. This helps to keep:

• [_____]
• [_____]

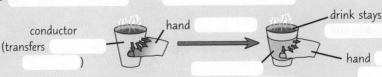

conductor
(transfers [_____])

hand [_____]

drink stays [_____]

hand [_____]

(e.g. cardboard or [_____])

 ☑ ☑ ☑

Section 8 — Energy and Matter

Heating

Thermal Equilibrium

Hotter objects

The hotter object

and

the

Energy transfer continues

THERMAL EQUILIBRIUM —

Conduction

CONDUCTION — process where

Particles

when they bump into

The objects

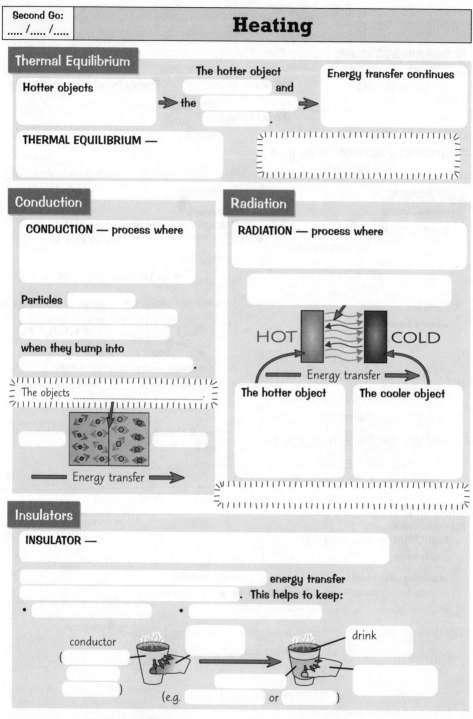

Energy transfer

Radiation

RADIATION — process where

HOT COLD

Energy transfer

The hotter object

The cooler object

Insulators

INSULATOR —

energy transfer

. This helps to keep:

•

•

conductor

( )

(e.g. or)

drink

Mixed Practice Quizzes

There's still a good chunk of Section 8 to do, but it's time to test your knowledge of p.91-96. Hopefully you've stored up enough energy to tackle these quizzes.

Quiz 1   Date: ...... / ...... / ......

1) Give an example of something that has energy in its chemical energy store. ☑

2) True or false? The hotter an object gets, the more energy it radiates. ☑

3) What is the relationship between energy transferred (or work done), force and distance moved? ☑

4) What is meant by the 'conservation of energy'? ☑

5) Which energy store do all moving objects have some energy stored in? ☑

6) Define the term 'thermal equilibrium'. ☑

7) Name a method of heating that can take place without objects touching. ☑

8) True or false? Insulation is only used to keep objects hot. ☑

Total:

Quiz 2   Date: ...... / ...... / ......

1) Give four examples of types of energy store. ☑

2) How is energy normally wasted as part of an energy transfer? ☑

3) Explain briefly why two objects at different temperatures will eventually reach thermal equilibrium. ☑

4) What is meant by the term 'insulator'? ☑

5) True or false? The higher an object's temperature, the more energy in its thermal energy store. ☑

6) Give two ways energy can be transferred by heating. ☑

7) Give two examples of situations where energy in chemical stores is transferred to thermal energy stores. ☑

8) True or false? To transfer a set amount of energy over a shorter distance, a larger force must be applied. ☑

Total:

Mixed Practice Quizzes

Quiz 3 Date: ...... / ...... / ......

1) True or false? All energy transfers waste some energy. ☑

2) What does an object supplying a force need in order to move something? ☑

3) Name a method of heating that can only take place if objects are touching. ☑

4) Give two energy stores that the energy
   in food is transferred to during metabolism. ☑

5) How is energy transferred electrically? ☑

6) True or false? When an object moves closer to the ground,
   its gravitational potential energy store increases. ☑

7) Describe the effect of adding an insulating layer
   to a cup containing a hot drink. ☑

8) Which energy store does everything have some energy stored in? ☑

Total: _____

Quiz 4 Date: ...... / ...... / ......

1) How is energy transferred by light and sound? ☑

2) Describe the transfer of energy between stores that happens
   when a stretched out spring is released. ☑

3) True or false? In an energy transfer, the store
   that energy is transferred from decreases. ☑

4) When will an object emit more energy by radiation —
   when it is hot or when it is cold? ☑

5) True or false? Energy is only useful when being transferred between stores. ☑

6) Describe the energy transfer that takes place when fuel is burned. ☑

7) When heating a saucepan, which energy store
   is the wasted energy transferred to? ☑

8) Explain how energy is transferred by conduction. ☑

Total: _____

Energy Resources

Six Energy Resources

The Sun supplies [_____] on Earth —
it is [_____] before we use it.

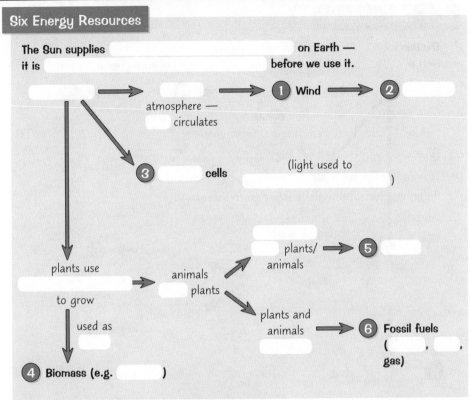

[_____] → [_____] → **1** Wind → **2** [_____]

atmosphere —
[____] circulates

3 [_____] cells [_____] (light used to [_____])

plants use [_____] → animals [____] plants

[_____] plants/ animals → **5** [_____]

to grow

used as [_____]

plants and animals → **6** Fossil fuels ([____], [____], gas)

4 Biomass (e.g. [_____])

Renewable and Non-Renewable Resources

We use [_____] for things such as:

• generating [_____] • [_____] • transport

NON-RENEWABLE RESOURCES	Energy resources that will [_____].	E.g. [_____] (take [_____] to replenish)
RENEWABLE RESOURCES	Energy resources that will [_____].	E.g. [____] energy, wind, [____], plants

One problem with .... resources is ....
— e.g. it's not always ....

Section 8 — Energy and Matter

Energy Resources

Six Energy Resources

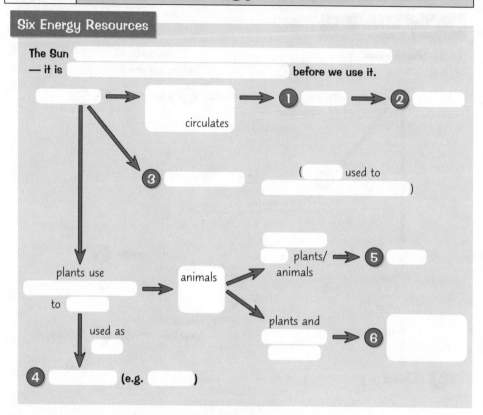

The Sun _____
— it is _____ **before we use it.**

_____ → circulates → **1** _____ → **2** _____

3 _____ (_____ used to _____)

plants use _____
to _____ → animals → plants/ animals → **5** _____

used as _____

plants and _____ → **6** _____

4 _____ (e.g. _____)

Renewable and Non-Renewable Resources

We use _____ :

• _____   • _____   • _____

NON-RENEWABLE RESOURCES	Energy resources that will	
		to replenish)
RENEWABLE RESOURCES		E.g.

One problem with _____
— e.g. it's not _____ .

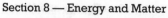 

Cost of Electricity and Energy Values

Calculating Energy Transfer

ELECTRICAL APPLIANCE — anything that needs [_____].

Appliances transfer [_____] [_____] to other stores.

POWER RATING — amount of energy an [_____] [_____] when working at its recommended [_____].

[_____] transferred   Power — [_____] is transferred.

Equation		.... =	P	×	t		[_____]
Units	.........., J	watts, ...			.........., s		
	kilowatt-hours, ...	...................., kW			...................., h		

Electricity at Home

[_____] amount of energy transferred in [_____].

[_____] in a time period = meter reading [_____] − [_____] at start

This is then used to [_____].

[_____] energy transferred

[_____] = E × price

per [_____]

[_____]
[_____] cost more to run — they [_____] in a set time period.

Energy in Food

All food contains [_____] — we need to [_____]
[_____] each day.

Food labels tell you [_____] is in the food, measured in [_____].

You can use this information to [_____].

 ☑ ☑ ☑

Second Go: ..... /..... /..... Cost of Electricity and Energy Values

Calculating Energy Transfer

ELECTRICAL APPLIANCE —

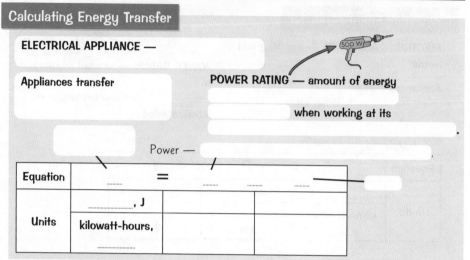

Appliances transfer

POWER RATING — amount of energy

when working at its

.

Power —

Equation	....	=	....	....	....	
Units	........, J					
	kilowatt-hours, ...					

Electricity at Home

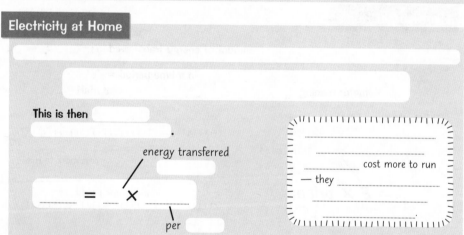

This is then

.

energy transferred

.... = ... × ....

per

— they .... cost more to run

....

Energy in Food

All food contains

Food labels

, measured in .

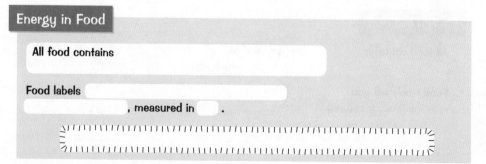

Physical Changes

The Three States of Matter

 1

 2

 3

Physical vs Chemical Changes

Physical changes .... from
.... in that:

No .... happens.

No .... are made.

Six Physical Processes

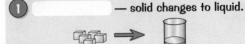 1 .... — solid changes to liquid.

2 **FREEZING** — .... changes to ....

3 **EVAPORATING** — .... changes to ....

 4 .... —
gas changes to liquid.

5 **SUBLIMATION** — .... changes to ....

 6 **DISSOLVING** — solid ....
.... to form a solution.

All of these processes are .... (they can be
...........................).
E.g. melting is undone by ....

Conservation of Mass

.... changes don't involve ....

E.g.

**20 g
Ice**

 ....
Freezing

 ....
Condensing

**20 g
Water**

....

| Second Go:
...../...../..... | **Physical Changes** |

The Three States of Matter

1

2

3

Physical vs Chemical Changes

....
....
....:

| happens. |

| No |

Six Physical Processes

1 _____ — solid changes to liquid.

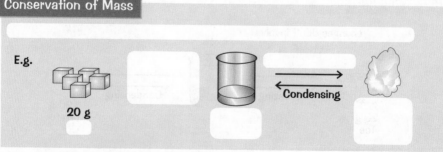

2 _____

3 EVAPORATING — ____ changes to ____ .

4 _____

5 _____

6 DISSOLVING — _____

All of these _____ (they can be
_____). E.g. melting
is _____ .

Conservation of Mass

E.g.

20 g

Condensing

Movement of Particles

Properties of Solids, Liquids and Gases

This means solids are

	Distance between particles	Particle ....
Solids	.... (very high density) Small (...............)	.... (can't flow) Slow (....... flow)
Gases	Large (...............)	

.... — when ice melts its particles ...., so ice is .... than water.

Brownian Motion

BROWNIAN MOTION — the [   ] of any particle suspended ([   ]) in [   ].

[   ] motion of large particle.

gas, e.g. [   ]

Particles can be [   ] or [   ].

[   ] changes in direction.

Diffusion

DIFFUSION — the [   ] of particles from [   ] concentration, caused by their [   ].

[   ] concentration of darker particles

[   ] concentration of darker particles

even concentration

Changes in Temperature

Higher temperature

Particles [   ]

[   ]

particles increase

Substance [   ]

E.g. when [   ] is heated, it [   ] up the tube.

If you ...., it will cause it to change ....

Movement of Particles

Properties of Solids, Liquids and Gases

This means

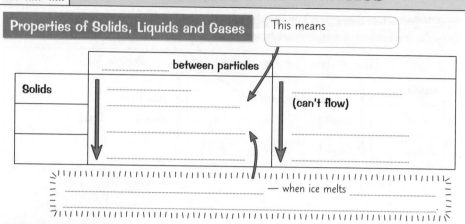

	between particles	
Solids		(can't flow)

— when ice melts

Brownian Motion

BROWNIAN MOTION —

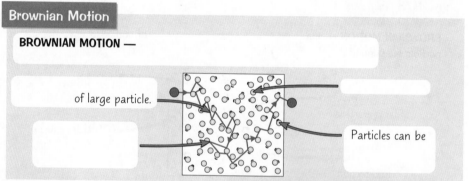

of large particle.

Particles can be

Diffusion

DIFFUSION —

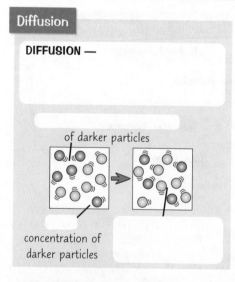

of darker particles

concentration of
darker particles

Changes in Temperature

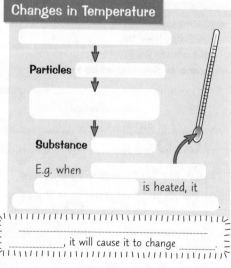

Particles

Substance

E.g. when

is heated, it

, it will cause it to change

Section 8 — Energy and Matter

Mixed Practice Quizzes

Well, there was plenty to learn on p.99-106. Luckily, there are some quick quiz questions here to help make sure your knowledge isn't an unreliable resource.

Quiz 1 Date: ...... / ...... / ......

1) Define the term 'power rating'.

2) What physical process involves a solid changing to a gas?

3) True or false? When a substance freezes, its mass doesn't change.

4) What are the three states of matter?

5) True or false? We are able to use the wind as an energy resource.

6) Give the unit that is often used to measure the energy content of foods.

7) Why does the level of liquid in a thermometer change when its temperature increases?

8) Describe one problem with relying on renewable energy resources.

Total:

Quiz 2 Date: ...... / ...... / ......

1) What device is used in homes to work out the amount of energy transferred in a time period?

2) What quantity is measured in kWh?

3) Give three examples of energy resources that are renewable.

4) Describe how particle motion in solids and liquids is different.

5) Describe one way in which a physical change is different from a chemical change.

6) What two things must be multiplied together to work out the energy transferred by an appliance?

7) True or false? Ice is more dense than water.

8) Which physical process is the opposite of melting?

Total:

Mixed Practice Quizzes

Quiz 3 Date: ...... / ...... / ......

1) What supplies almost all of the energy on Earth? ☑
2) Name six examples of physical processes. ☑
3) What is an example of a type of biomass that can be used as fuel? ☑
4) What is an electrical appliance? ☑
5) Describe what happens in the process of dissolving. ☑
6) What units for power rating and time do you need to use
   in order to calculate energy transferred in joules? ☑
7) What is Brownian motion? ☑
8) Name the process in which particles spread out from an area
   of high concentration to an area of low concentration. ☑

Total: ☐

Quiz 4 Date: ...... / ...... / ......

1) Give an example of a pair of opposite physical processes. ☑
2) True or false? An appliance with a lower power rating will cost more
   to run in a set time period than an appliance with a higher power rating. ☑
3) What is the formula used to calculate fuel bills? ☑
4) What term describes resources that will run out one day? ☑
5) Describe how the distance between particles changes
   when a substance changes state from liquid to gas. ☑
6) Give two examples of fossil fuels. ☑
7) What causes a particle moving with Brownian motion to change direction? ☑
8) How can plants and animals be used as an energy resource
   without waiting a long time for them to form fossil fuels? ☑

Total: ☐

Speed

First Go:
..... / ..... / .....

Calculating Speed

SPEED — a measure of

_____

in a set amount of time.

$$Speed = \frac{\rule{3cm}{0.4pt}}{\rule{3cm}{0.4pt}}$$

Three _____ for speed:

① _____ m/s

② miles per hour _____ or _____

③ _____

Relative Motion

RELATIVE SPEED — _____

_____ from the perspective

of _____ .

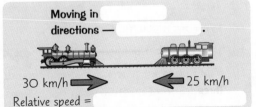

Moving in _____ directions — _____ .

30 km/h ➡   ⬅ 25 km/h

Relative speed = _____

Moving in _____ direction — _____ .

20 mph ➡   30 mph ➡

Relative speed = _____

These two rules only work for objects moving

_____ .

Distance-Time Graphs

DISTANCE-TIME GRAPH — _____

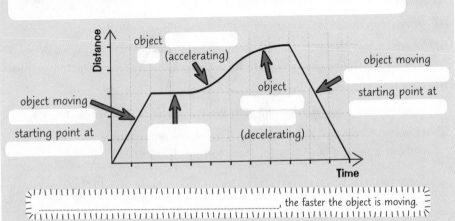

object _____ (accelerating)

object (decelerating)

object moving _____

starting point at _____

object moving _____

starting point at _____

_____ , the faster the object is moving.

 ☑   ☑   ☺ ☑

Second Go:
..... / ..... / .....

Speed

Calculating Speed

SPEED —

[ ]

[ ] = ———————
[ ]

Three

1 ___ m/s

2 [ ]

3 [ ]

Relative Motion

RELATIVE SPEED —

[ ]

30 km/h ➡️   ⬅️ 25 km/h

Relative speed = [ ]

[ ]

20 mph ➡️   30 mph ➡️

Relative speed = [ ]

These two rules only work for _____
_____ .

Distance-Time Graphs

DISTANCE-TIME GRAPH —

[ ]

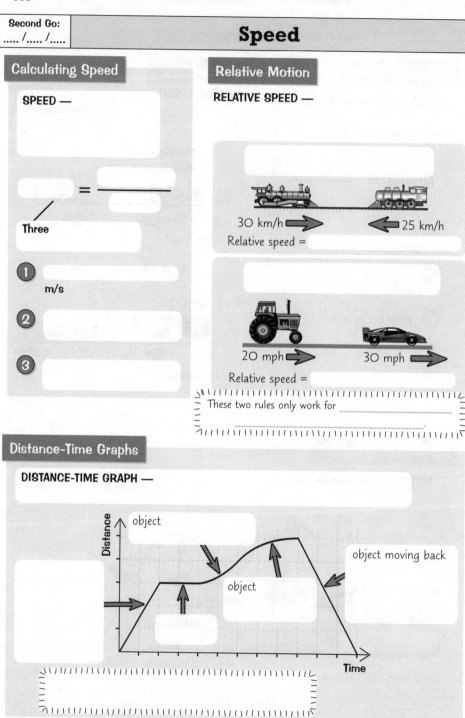

object [ ]

object [ ]

object moving back

Distance (y-axis) / Time (x-axis)

Forces and Movement

Forces

FORCE — on an object caused by it

.

Force is measured in

.

Forces:

- usually

- always act in a

-

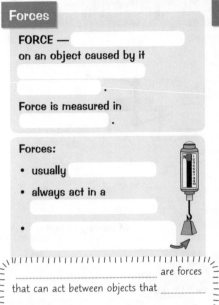

_____ are forces that can act between objects that _____ .

Balanced and Unbalanced Forces

Balanced forces produce

.

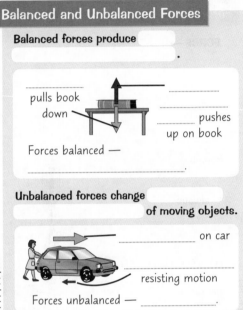

pulls book down

_____ pushes up on book

Forces balanced —

Unbalanced forces change

of moving objects.

on car

resisting motion

Forces unbalanced — _____ .

Five Things Forces can Make Objects Do

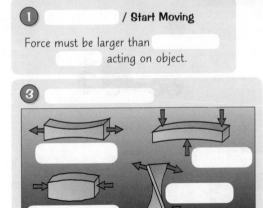

1 _____ / Start Moving

Force must be larger than _____ acting on object.

2 _____ /
Stop Moving

_____ resistance

must be larger than

3

4 _____ Direction

Force must be in _____ to object's original direction.

The size _____ of the force determine _____ .

5

Section 9 — Forces and Motion

Forces and Movement

Forces

FORCE —

Force is

Forces:
-
- always
-

.... are forces that can act ....

Balanced and Unbalanced Forces

Forces .... —

of moving objects.

Forces .... —

Five Things Forces can Make Objects Do

1

Force must

2

must be

3

4

Force must

.... of the force ....

5

Force Diagrams

Arrows in Force Diagrams

FORCE DIAGRAM — a diagram that shows the _____.

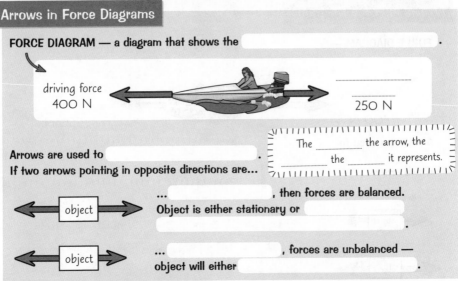

driving force
400 N

250 N

Arrows are used to _____.
If two arrows pointing in opposite directions are...

The _____ the arrow, the _____ the _____ it represents.

... _____, then forces are balanced.
Object is either stationary or _____.

object

... _____, forces are unbalanced —
object will either _____.

object

Two Rules for Calculating Overall Force from Force Diagrams

① Subtract forces acting in _____.

② Add forces acting in _____.

This only works for forces acting _____ (in 'one dimension').

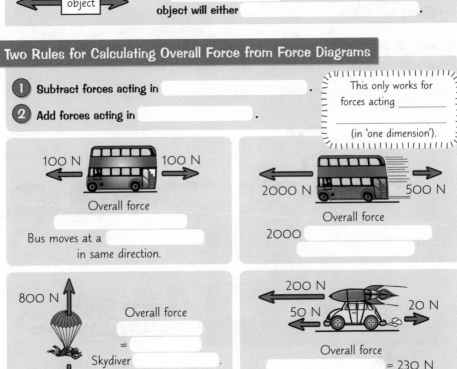

100 N   100 N

Overall force
_____

Bus moves at a _____
in same direction.

2000 N   500 N

Overall force

2000 _____
_____

800 N

Overall force
_____
=
Skydiver _____.

600 N

200 N
50 N   20 N

Overall force
_____ = 230 N

Section 9 — Forces and Motion

Force Diagrams

Arrows in Force Diagrams

FORCE DIAGRAM —

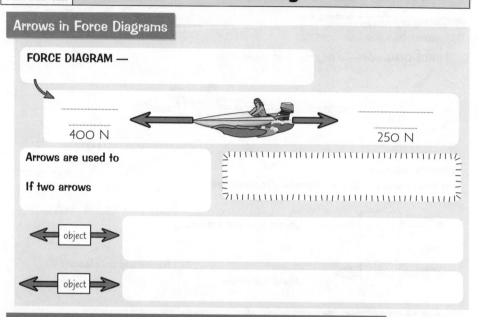

....

....
400 N

....
250 N

Arrows are used to

If two arrows

⟨— object —⟩

⟨— object —⟩

Two Rules for Calculating Overall Force from Force Diagrams

1 ....

acting in ....

2 .... acting in ....

This only works for ....

....

....

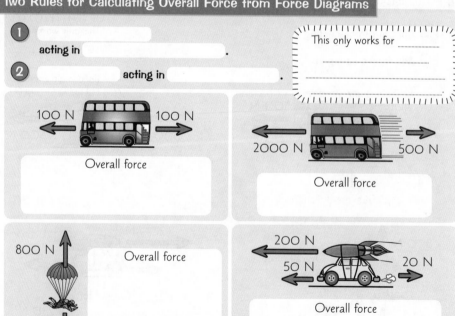

100 N ⟵ 🚌 ⟶ 100 N

Overall force

2000 N ⟵ 🚌 ⟶ 500 N

Overall force

800 N ↑
🪂
Overall force

600 N ↓

200 N ⟵ 🚗
50 N ⟵ ⟶ 20 N

Overall force

Frictional Forces and Moments

Frictional Forces

FRICTIONAL FORCE — a force that acts in _____ .

Frictional forces always try to _____ .

Three frictional forces:

1. Friction (_____)

E.g. box and ground
____ force
FRAGILE
To ____ an object out of the way, you need to ____ .

2. Air resistance

These are also called

3. ____

Air Resistance when Skydiving

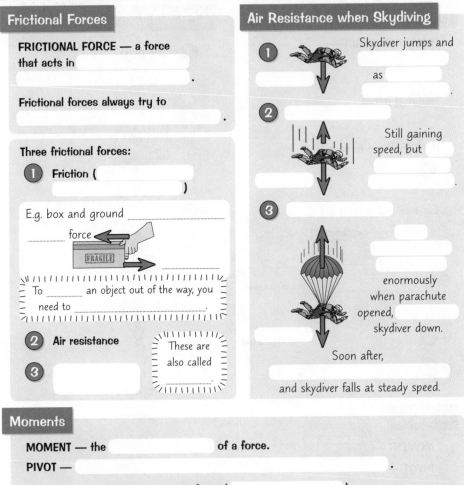

1. Skydiver jumps and ____ as ____ .

2. ____ Still gaining speed, but ____ .

3. ____ ____ enormously when parachute opened, ____ skydiver down.

Soon after, ____ and skydiver falls at steady speed.

Moments

MOMENT — the _____ of a force.

PIVOT — _____ .

force (_____)

____ $= F \times d$

(_____ , Nm) from the _____ (in metres, m)

No change in movement if _____
(anticlockwise moments = _____)

If moments ____ ____ , object turns in direction of ____ .

anticlockwise

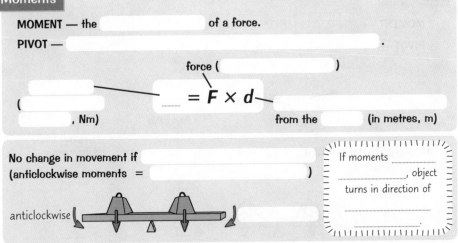

Second Go:
...../...../.....

Frictional Forces and Moments

Frictional Forces

FRICTIONAL FORCE —

Frictional forces

.

Three frictional forces:

1

E.g. box and ground

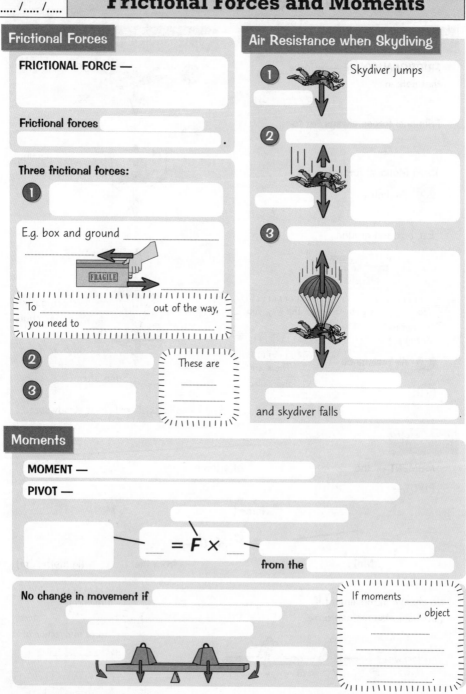

To _____ out of the way,
you need to _____ .

These are
_____
_____
_____ .

2

3

Air Resistance when Skydiving

1   Skydiver jumps

2

3

and skydiver falls

Moments

MOMENT —

PIVOT —

_____ = **F** × _____

from the

No change in movement if

If moments _____
_____, object
_____
_____
_____ .

Section 9 — Forces and Motion

Forces and Elasticity

Stretching and Compressing

Forces can stretch or compress (squash) objects, [_____] [_____] .

When forces deform an object, [_____] , e.g:

A spring is [_____] . → Energy transferred from [_____] energy store to [_____] potential energy store.

When spring 'springs' back into [_____] , energy transferred back to [_____] energy store.

ELASTIC OBJECT — an object that [_____] after forces [_____] (e.g. a spring).

Springs in Equilibrium

Forces are [_____]

if stretched/compressed spring

force of weight =

forces in

Hooke's Law

The extension of a spring, e, is [_____] [_____] .

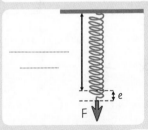

([_____])

[_____] $= k \times e$ —([_____])

[_____]

(in Newton metres, [_____])

I.e. the relationship between [_____] [_____] .

Force / Extension

Only some objects obey [_____] (e.g. springs) and it only works up to [_____] (this force is [_____] than for most [_____]).

Forces and Elasticity

Stretching and Compressing

Forces can

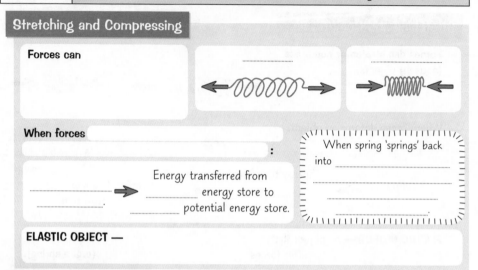

When forces

:

When spring 'springs' back
into

Energy transferred from
_____ energy store to
_____ potential energy store.

ELASTIC OBJECT —

Springs in Equilibrium

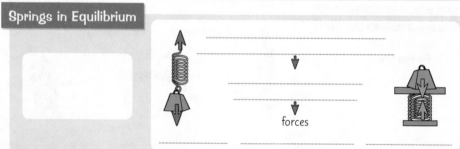

forces

Hooke's Law

The _____ of a spring,

.

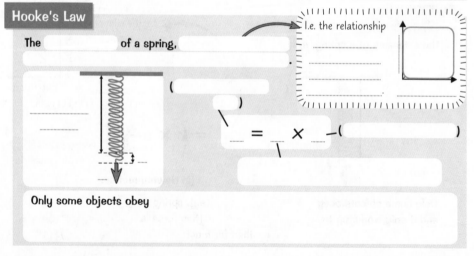

(

)

i.e. the relationship

_____ = _____ × –( )

Only some objects obey

Pressure

Calculating Pressure

PRESSURE — a measure of [____] [____] is put [____].

The force acts [____] (at 90°) to the [____].

in [____]

$$Pressure = \frac{}{}$$

in metres squared, [____]

in pascals, Pa
OR

[____]

1 Pa = [____]

Pressure in Liquids

Pressure [____] as depth [____].

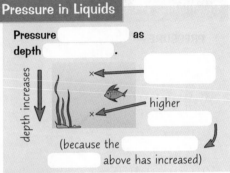

higher [____]

(because the [____] above has increased)

depth increases

Upthrust

UPTHRUST — the overall [____] on an object in water, due to [____] being greater at [____] than at the top.

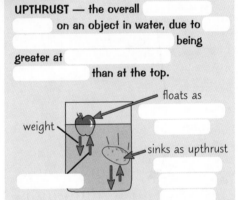

floats as [____]

weight [____]

sinks as upthrust [____]

Atmospheric Pressure

THE ATMOSPHERE — the layer of [____] that [____].

[____] atmospheric pressure

[____] atmospheric pressure

The [____] you go. → The [____] atmosphere [____]. → The [____] there is [____] on you. → The [____] the atmospheric pressure.

And vice versa, [____], the [____] the atmospheric pressure.

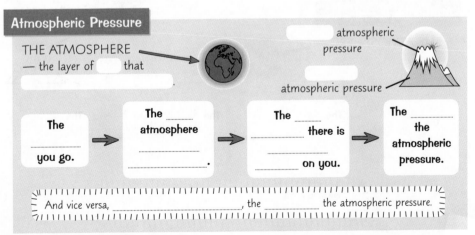

Pressure

Calculating Pressure

PRESSURE —

The force acts
....
....
....

= _____

Pressure in Liquids

increases

pressure

pressure

(because _____)

Upthrust

UPTHRUST —

on an object in water,

than at the top.

as upthrust

Atmospheric Pressure

THE ATMOSPHERE —

The

The

The

The

And vice versa, _____
....

Mixed Practice Quizzes

These quizzes test p.109-120. You can do them in your own time — there's no pressure. Well, there is pressure but not *pressure*. Oh, just ignore me.

Quiz 1   Date: ...... / ...... / ......

1) True or false? Hooke's Law works up to a much higher force for springs than for most other materials.

2) Define 'upthrust'.

3) If a force diagram shows two forces acting on an object in the same direction, how can the overall force acting on the object be calculated?

4) What formula links pressure, force and area?

5) What is meant by 'relative motion'?

6) True or false? Unbalanced forces produce no change in movement.

7) Give three common units used for speed.

8) When are forces 'in equilibrium'?

Total:

Quiz 2   Date: ...... / ...... / ......

1) State three things that forces can make objects do.

2) Define 'pressure'.

3) Why do skydivers slow down when they open a parachute?

4) True or false? Hooke's Law says that the relationship between force and extension is non-linear.

5) What instrument can be used to measure force?

6) What formula links speed, distance and time?

7) What is meant by a 'frictional force'?

8) True or false? When anticlockwise moments equal clockwise moments there is no change in movement.

Total:

Mixed Practice Quizzes

Quiz 3 | Date: ...... / ...... / ......

1) What equation links moment, force and perpendicular distance?

2) Name two frictional forces.

3) Explain how pressure in liquids changes with increased depth.

4) What is meant by an 'elastic object'?

5) How do you work out the speed of an object relative to a second object, which is moving along the same straight line in the opposite direction?

6) True or false? The steeper the slope of a distance-time graph, the slower the object is moving.

7) True or false? Objects sink when their weight is equal to upthrust.

8) Define 'force'.

Total:

Quiz 4 | Date: ...... / ...... / ......

1) What is meant by a 'moment'?

2) How does Hooke's Law link force, spring constant and extension?

3) Explain how atmospheric pressure changes with increased height.

4) True or false? A flat line on a distance-time graph means an object has stopped moving.

5) State two different units for pressure.

6) Define 'speed'.

7) True or false? If two same-sized forces act on an object in opposite directions, then the object is either stationary or moving at a steady speed in one direction.

8) What energy store is energy transferred to when a spring is stretched?

Total:

Water Waves

First Go:
..... / ..... / .....

Transverse Waves

Waves transfer energy [_____].

TRANSVERSE WAVE — a wave with undulations ([_____])
that are at [_____] to the direction of [_____].

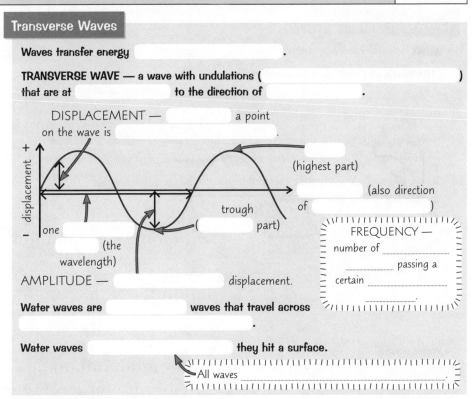

DISPLACEMENT — [_____] a point
on the wave is [_____].

+ displacement

one [_____] (the wavelength)

[_____] (highest part)

trough ([_____] part)

[_____] (also direction of [_____])

AMPLITUDE — [_____] displacement.

FREQUENCY — number of _____ passing a certain _____.

Water waves are [_____] waves that travel across [_____].

Water waves [_____] they hit a surface.

All waves _____.

Superposition

SUPERPOSITION — the [_____] of two waves
combine [_____].

What meets?	Before meeting:	When meeting:	After meeting:
Two [_____]		big crest	
Two troughs		big [_____]	
Crest [_____] [_____]		[_____] cancel out	

(if the [_____] have the same [_____])

Water Waves

Transverse Waves

Waves _____.

TRANSVERSE WAVE — a wave with

_____

_____ a point

on the wave is _____.

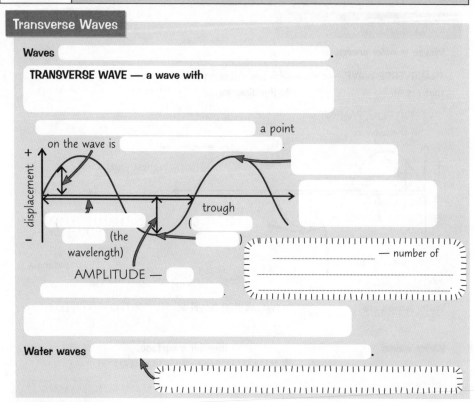

displacement + / −

trough
(   )

(the wavelength)

AMPLITUDE —

_____ — number of

Water waves _____.

Superposition

_____ of two waves
_____.

What meets?	Before meeting:	When meeting:	After meeting:
		big crest	
troughs			

(if _____)

Light Waves and Reflection

Light Waves vs Water Waves

LIGHT — a wave produced by ....,
.... in a straight line.

	Water waves	Light waves
.... waves?	Yes	
Transfer energy?		Yes
Can be .... ?		
Need .... to travel?	Yes	

The Speed of Light

.... in a vacuum —
a vacuum ....,
so there's nothing that can ....

.... a vacuum.

speed of light in a vacuum = ... ⎯ three hundred million
....

Two Types of Reflection

Light waves (.......)
reflect ....

① **SPECULAR REFLECTION** —
.... at the
same .... along the surface.

........................., shiny
surface (e.g. a
..............) — gives a
....

② **DIFFUSE REFLECTION** —
.... are reflected in
.... directions
(................) along the surface.

rough, ...
surface
(e.g. ....)

Ray Diagrams

incident
ray

angle of
....

....

(90° to
........................)

angle of
reflection

....

ray

....
surface

angle of incidence =
angle of ....

When drawing ....,
.... to measure
angles and .... to make sure
all lines are ....

Light Waves and Reflection

Light Waves vs Water Waves

LIGHT —

	Water waves	Light waves
	Yes	
Transfer ?		
Can be ?		
Need		

The Speed of Light

— a vacuum ,
so there's .

speed of light .... = three hundred million

Two Types of Reflection

Light waves

1. **SPECULAR REFLECTION —**

2. along the surface.

rough,

Ray Diagrams

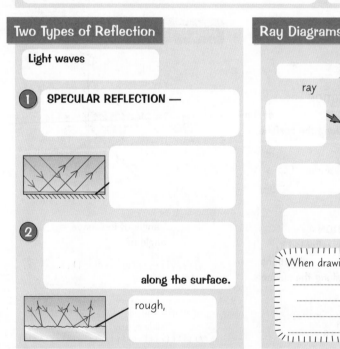

ray

angle of

surface

When drawing ....
....
.... to make sure

Refraction, Lenses and Cameras

Refraction

REFRACTION — when [ ] changes direction
([ ]) as it crosses a boundary [ ]
.

A medium is
....
.... travels through.

[ ] through transparent ([ ]) materials like [ ] .

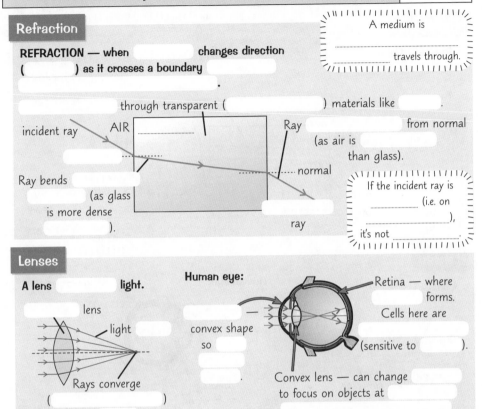

incident ray

AIR

Ray [ ] from normal
(as air is [ ]
than glass).

Ray bends [ ]
(as glass
is more dense
[ ]).

.... normal

ray

If the incident ray is
.... (i.e. on
........................),
it's not ....

Lenses

A lens [ ] **light.**

[ ] lens

[ ] light

Rays converge
([ ])
at a [ ] .

Human eye:

[ ] —
convex shape
so [ ]
.

Retina — where
[ ] forms.
Cells here are
[ ]
(sensitive to [ ]).

Convex lens — can change
to focus on objects at [ ]

The Pinhole Camera

photographic [ ] camera [ ]

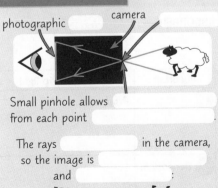

Small pinhole allows [ ]
from each point [ ]
.

The rays [ ] in the camera,
so the image is [ ]
and [ ]

Two Examples of Absorbers

ABSORBER — anything that absorbs the
....
....

Absorber	Response to light
1 [ ] cells	**Produce** [ ] [ ] signals that are sent to the [ ] .
2 Sensors in [ ]	**Produce** [ ] that are read by computers.

 ☑ ☑ ☑

Refraction, Lenses and Cameras

Refraction

REFRACTION —

A medium is _____
_____.

_____ through transparent
_____.

_____ (as air is
_____).

ray

AIR

_____

(as glass is more
dense _____).

If the incident ray is
_____ (i.e. on
_____),
it's not _____.

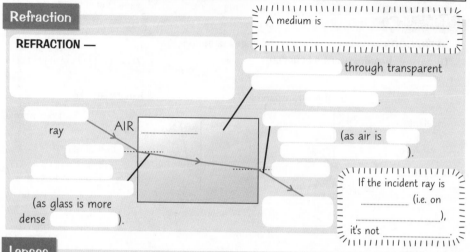

Lenses

A lens _____.

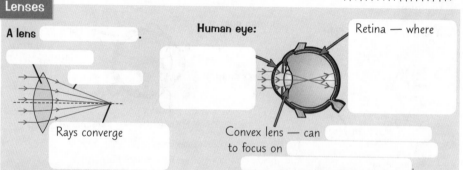

Rays converge

Human eye:

Retina — where

Convex lens — can _____
to focus on _____

The Pinhole Camera

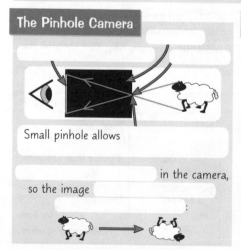

Small pinhole allows _____

_____ in the camera,
so the image _____.

Two Examples of Absorbers

ABSORBER —

Absorber	Response to light
1	Produce
2 Sensors in	
	read by computers.

Colour

The Light Spectrum

White light is a _____ .
It gets dispersed (_____)
when it _____ .

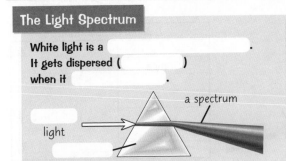

a spectrum

_____ light

Colours of spectrum:

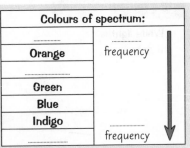

....	
Orange	frequency
....	
Green	
Blue	
Indigo	
....	frequency

Reflection and Absorption

_____ get reflected or absorbed by _____ .

This determines _____ of objects:

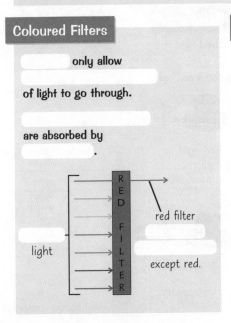

Apple looks red as it _____

except red, which is _____

Black objects absorb _____ .

_____ objects diffusely reflect _____

Coloured Filters

_____ only allow

_____ of light to go through.

_____

are absorbed by

_____ .

_____ light

red filter

_____ except red.

Coloured Light

Coloured light makes objects

_____ .

E.g. for a red hat:

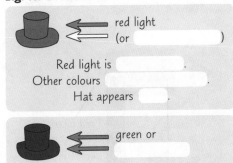

red light (or _____)

Red light is _____ .
Other colours _____ .
Hat appears _____ .

green or _____

_____ to reflect.

Other _____

Hat appears black.

Colour

The Light Spectrum

White light is

It gets

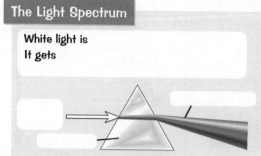

Colours of spectrum:	
	....
Orange	....
Indigo	....
	....

Reflection and Absorption

get reflected or   .

This determines   of objects:

Black objects

Apple looks red

, which is

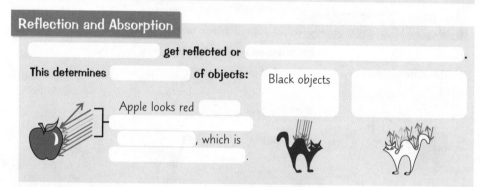

Coloured Filters

to go through.

red filter

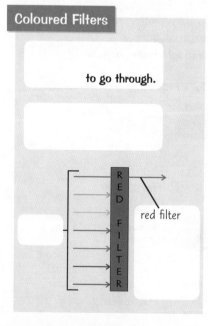

Coloured Light

Coloured light ....

....

E.g. for a red hat:

Red light

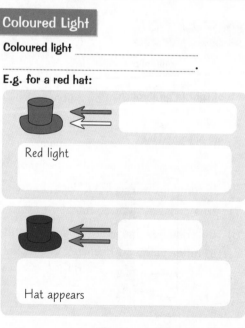

Hat appears

Mixed Practice Quizzes

Sorry to interrupt you partway through Section 10, but it's time for some reflection. Try these quizzes to see how much you've absorbed from pages p.123-130.

Quiz 1   Date: ...... / ...... / ......

1) Give two similarities between water waves and light waves.

2) True or false? On a ray diagram, the angle of incidence is equal to the angle of reflection.

3) Describe what happens to white light when it hits a red filter.

4) In terms of waves, what is meant by 'displacement'?

5) Explain why a red object would appear black under green light.

6) State how the image of an object from a pinhole camera is different to how the object really appears.

7) Name a part of the eye that can focus light.

8) Describe what a 'transverse wave' is.

Total:

Quiz 2   Date: ...... / ...... / ......

1) What is meant by the term 'superposition'?

2) What is the name of the point where light rays converge after being refracted by a convex lens?

3) What is light?

4) What does 'photosensitive' mean?

5) Describe what happens to a beam of white light when it hits a prism.

6) In terms of waves, what does 'frequency' mean?

7) True or false? Waves transfer energy from place to place.

8) Describe how these absorbers respond to light:
a) retina cells,   b) sensors in a digital camera.

Total:

Mixed Practice Quizzes

Quiz 3   Date: ...... / ...... / ......

1) Describe what will happen when the crests of two waves that are travelling in opposite directions meet.

2) True or false? White objects do not reflect any colours.

3) What is refraction?

4) Why do light waves travel fastest through a vacuum?

5) Explain why a red object appears red when in white light.

6) How are light waves reflected by a mirror — by specular reflection or diffuse reflection?

7) In terms of waves, what is meant by 'amplitude'?

8) Which colours are absorbed by an object that appears black in white light?

Total:

Quiz 4   Date: ...... / ...... / ......

1) Which colour in the spectrum has the highest frequency?

2) What is the speed of light in a vacuum (in metres per second)?

3) What happens when the crest of one water wave meets the trough of another water wave with the same amplitude?

4) What does 'normal' mean when it refers to reflection or refraction?

5) What causes the image from a pinhole camera to be upside down and crossed over?

6) Define the following terms: a) specular reflection, b) diffuse reflection.

7) True or false? All waves can be reflected by surfaces.

8) Which way is light refracted when it moves from a less dense to a more dense medium — towards the normal or away from the normal?

Total:

Sound Waves

Longitudinal Waves

LONGITUDINAL WAVE — a wave with
_____ that are parallel to
_____
_____ .

E.g. _____
in a slinky _____ :

vibrations

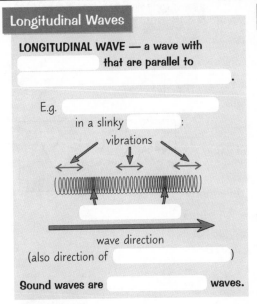

_____

wave direction

(also direction of _____)

Sound waves are _____ **waves.**

Reflection and Absorption

_____ **can be:**

- **Reflected**

ECHO — _____ being
reflected from _____ .

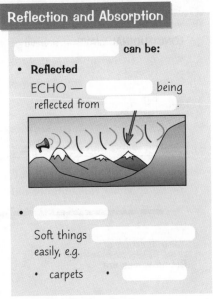

- _____

Soft things _____
easily, e.g.

- carpets - _____

Vibrations

Vibrating objects

_____

_____ :

_____

object

particles
vibrate

pressure   low pressure

vibrations cause _____

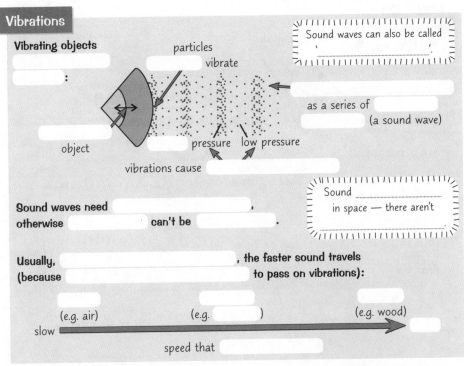

Sound waves can also be called
'_____ .'

_____
as a series of _____
_____ (a sound wave)

Sound _____
in space — there aren't
_____ .

Sound waves need _____ .
otherwise _____ **can't be** _____ .

Usually, _____ , **the faster sound travels**
(because _____ **to pass on vibrations):**

_____

(e.g. air)   (e.g. _____)   (e.g. wood)

slow _____

speed that _____

Sound Waves

Longitudinal Waves

LONGITUDINAL WAVE — a wave

E.g.

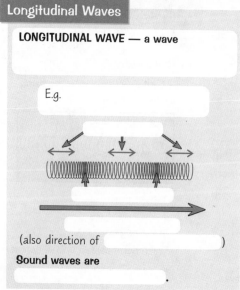

(also direction of ⬚)

Sound waves are

⬚ .

Reflection and Absorption

⬚ **can be:**

• ⬚

ECHO —

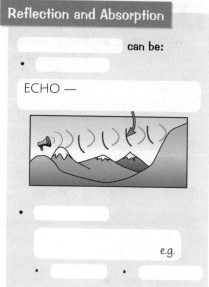

•

⬚ ⬚

e.g.

⬚ • ⬚

Vibrations

Vibrating objects

⬚

⬚ :

⬚

object

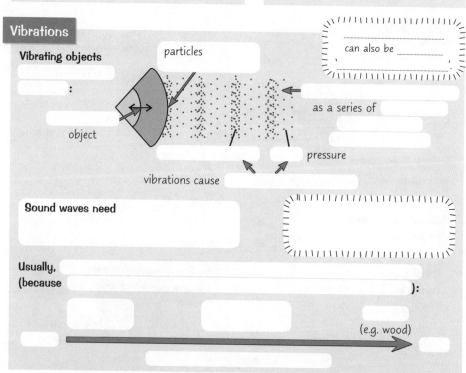

particles

can also be ⬚ ,

as a series of

pressure

vibrations cause

Sound waves need

Usually, (because ⬚):

(e.g. wood)

 ✓ ✓ ✓

Hearing

Frequency

The frequency of sound is [_____] sound waves
([_____]) that pass [_____].

Frequency is measured in [_____], Hz (1 Hz = [_____]).

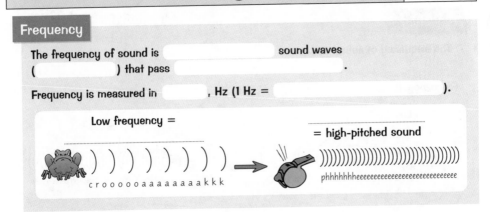

Low frequency = [_____]

[_____] = high-pitched sound

crooooooaaaaaaaakkk

phhhhhheeeeeeeeeeeeeeeeeeeeeeeeeeeeeeee

Auditory Ranges

AUDITORY RANGE — [_____] that a certain animal can hear.

[_____]

auditory range:
[____] – 20 000 Hz

[_____]

can hear frequencies [_____]

than 20 000 Hz, e.g.:

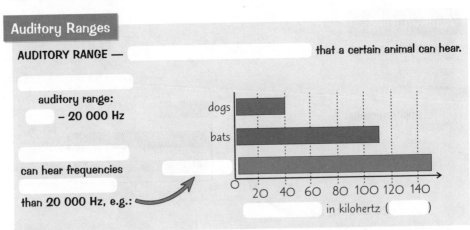

[_____] in kilohertz ([____])

dogs

bats

Hearing Sound Waves

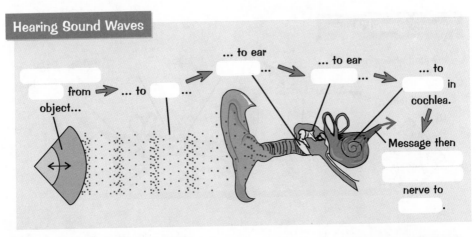

[_____] from ⇒ ... to [____] ...

... to ear [_____] ...

... to ear [_____] ...

... to [_____] in cochlea.

object...

Message then [_____]

nerve to [_____].

Hearing

Frequency

The frequency of sound is

Frequency is , Hz (1 Hz =).

Low _____ = _____ =

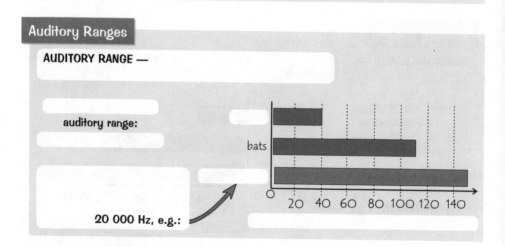

crooooooaaaaaaaakkk

phhhhhhheeeeeeeeeeeeeeeeeeeeeeeeeeee

Auditory Ranges

AUDITORY RANGE —

auditory range:

bats

20 000 Hz, e.g.:

O 20 40 60 80 100 120 140

Hearing Sound Waves

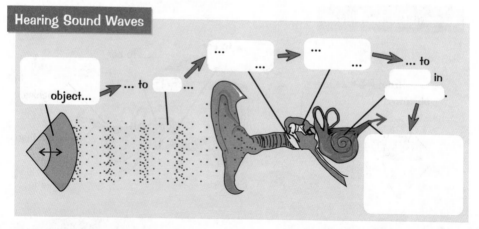

object... ... to ... ... to ... to

in

Uses of Sound Waves

Microphones

Microphones [_____] sound waves.

[_____]
hit microphone.

⬇

Diaphragm
[_____].

diaphragm — e.g.
[_____]
or plastic [_____]

⬇

Vibrations
[_____]
to [_____]
signals.

Another device can [_____]
[_____] so the sound can be
[_____].

Loudspeakers

Loudspeakers [_____] sound waves.

[_____] fed
into loudspeaker.

⬇

[_____]
vibrates.

⬇

Air vibrates,
[_____]
[_____].

Ultrasound

ULTRASOUND — sound with [_____] than 20 000 Hz
(higher than [_____]).

Two uses [_____]:

1 _____ objects,
e.g. _____
or false teeth.

➡ _____ from ultrasound
waves can _____
_____.

2 Physiotherapy ➡ Ultrasound could be used to
_____ in parts of _____
that are _____.

Scientists haven't _____
_____ to say this _____.

Uses of Sound Waves

Microphones

Microphones _____ .

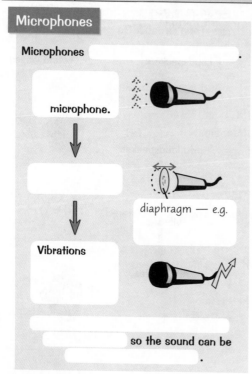

[_____]
microphone.

[_____]

Vibrations
[_____]

diaphragm — e.g.
[_____]

[_____] so the sound can be
[_____] .

Loudspeakers

Loudspeakers
[_____]

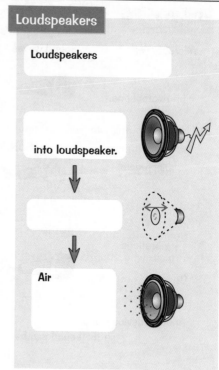

[_____]
into loudspeaker.

[_____]

Air [_____]

Ultrasound

ULTRASOUND —

Two _____ :

① [_____] ,
   e.g. [_____]
   [_____] . → ultrasound waves can [_____] .

② [_____] → Ultrasound could be
   [_____]

Mixed Practice Quizzes

Need something quick to help you remember stuff from p.133-138? I am at your service with some top-notch quizzes. They're fab. Go on, try 'em.

Quiz 1 — Date: ...... / ...... / ......

1) True or false? Loudspeakers convert sound waves into electrical signals.

2) Do sound waves travel faster in air or in water?

3) State two animals that can hear frequencies above a typical human's auditory range.

4) In longitudinal waves, are vibrations parallel or at a right angle to the direction of energy transfer?

5) True or false? Sound waves are created by vibrating objects.

6) Define ultrasound.

7) Explain why sound can't travel in space.

8) Describe how information in a sound wave is passed from a vibrating object to the brain.

Total:

Quiz 2 — Date: ...... / ...... / ......

1) Generally, how does the density of a medium affect the speed a sound wave travels through it?

2) What is an echo?

3) True or false? The frequency of a sound wave is the number of vibrations that pass a point per minute.

4) Name the first part of the ear that vibrates when a sound wave is heard.

5) Describe how sound waves are converted into electrical signals in a microphone.

6) What is meant by 'auditory range'?

7) Give an example of an object which absorbs sound waves easily.

8) What unit is frequency measured in?

Total:

Mixed Practice Quizzes

Quiz 3 Date: ...... / ...... / ......

1) Explain how ultrasound can be used to clean objects such as jewellery. ☑

2) True or false? A sound wave is vibrations being passed on as a series of pressure changes. ☑

3) What happens to the pitch of a sound when you increase the frequency? ☑

4) Do sound waves usually travel slower in solids or liquids? ☑

5) Do microphones detect or recreate sound waves? ☑

6) True or false? Sound waves need particles to travel. ☑

7) Describe what a 'longitudinal wave' is. ☑

8) Explain how a loudspeaker produces sound waves. ☑

Total:

Quiz 4 Date: ...... / ...... / ......

1) What is the typical human auditory range? ☑

2) True or false? When hearing a sound wave, the ear drum sends a message to the cochlea along the auditory nerve. ☑

3) Give one example of a longitudinal wave. ☑

4) What is the name given to sound with frequencies higher than 20 000 Hz? ☑

5) 'A sound reflected from a surface' is called what? ☑

6) True or false? Sound waves usually travel faster in gases than in liquids and solids. ☑

7) Which part of a loudspeaker vibrates when an electrical signal is fed into it? ☑

8) Why could ultrasound be useful in physiotherapy? ☑

Total:

Electric Current & Potential Difference

Electric Current

ELECTRIC CURRENT — the flow of

....

Current is measured in [   ] .

Electric current .... if the circuit is ....

Charges (negative ....) move

from [   ]

[   ] .

However, on circuit diagrams, current is

[   ]

from

[   ] .

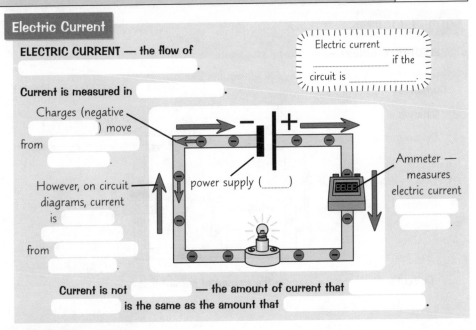

power supply (........)

Ammeter — measures electric current

Current is not [   ] — the amount of current that [   ]

[   ] is the same as the amount that [   ] .

Potential Difference

POTENTIAL DIFFERENCE — the [   ]

that [   ] round a circuit.

Potential difference is measured in [   ] .

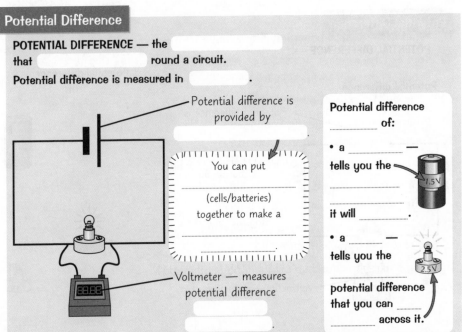

Potential difference is provided by

[   ]

You can put

....

....

(cells/batteries) together to make a

....

Voltmeter — measures potential difference

[   ] .

Potential difference of:

• a .... —
tells you the ....

....

it will ....

1.5V

• a .... —
tells you the ....

....

potential difference that you can ....

.... across it.

2.5V

Electric Current & Potential Difference

Electric Current

ELECTRIC CURRENT —

Current is _____ .

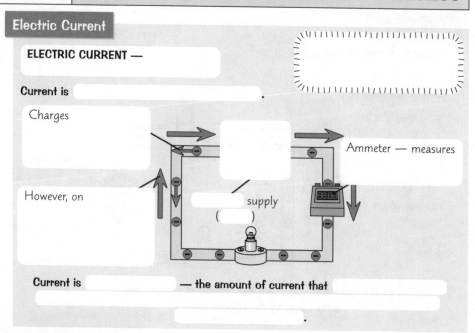

Charges

However, on

Ammeter — measures

supply
( )

Current is _____ — the amount of current that _____

Potential Difference

POTENTIAL DIFFERENCE —

Potential difference _____ .

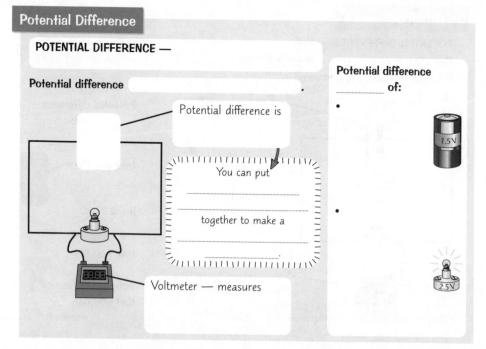

Potential difference is

You can put

....

together to make a

....

....

Potential difference
.... of:

•

1.5V

•

2.5V

Voltmeter — measures

Resistance and Circuit Symbols

Resistance

RESISTANCE — anything in [____] that slows down [____].

Resistance is measured in [____].

$$\textbf{Resistance} = \text{[\_\_\_\_]} \div \text{[\_\_\_\_]}$$

If resistance [____] and [____] stays the same, [____].

If potential difference [____] and [____] stays the same, [____].

Conductors

CONDUCTOR — a component or material that [____] [____] to pass through it.

e.g. metals

They have [____] resistance.

Insulators

INSULATOR — a component or material that [____] [____] to pass through it.

e.g. [____]

They have [____] resistance.

The lower [____] of a component, the better it is at [____].

E.g. a bulb with a [____] of 2 Ω is a [____] than a bulb with a [____] of 3 Ω.

Circuit Symbols

(a [____] energy source)

Battery
([____] cells put together)

Switch [____]

[____]
Voltmeter

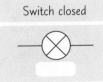

Switch closed

Motor

Buzzer

CIRCUIT DIAGRAM — a simplified drawing of a [____] using [____].

 ☑   ☑   ☑

Resistance and Circuit Symbols

Resistance

RESISTANCE —

Resistance is _____ .

_____

If _____
stays the same, _____ .

If _____
stays the same, _____ .

Conductors

_____

_____

They have _____ .

Insulators

INSULATOR — a component or material

_____

They have _____ .

The _____ ,
the better it is at _____ . E.g. a bulb
with a _____ is a _____
than a bulb with a _____ .

Circuit Symbols

(_____
cells put together)

(M)

CIRCUIT DIAGRAM — _____
_____ .

Section 11 — Electricity and Magnetism

Series and Parallel Circuits

Series Circuits

SERIES CIRCUIT — a circuit where the current has ☐☐☐☐☐☐☐.

In a series circuit, ☐☐☐☐ is the same ☐☐☐☐☐☐☐.

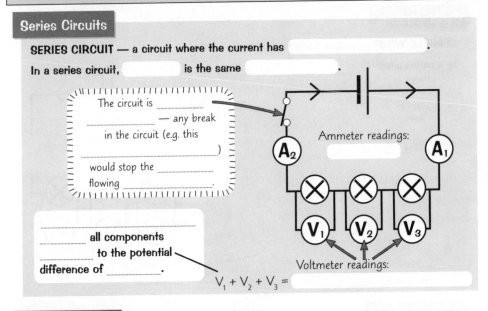

The circuit is _____
_____ — any break
in the circuit (e.g. this
_____)
would stop the _____
flowing _____.

Ammeter readings: ☐☐☐☐

A_2 A_1

V_1 V_2 V_3

_____ all components
_____ to the potential
difference of _____.

Voltmeter readings: ☐☐☐☐

$V_1 + V_2 + V_3 =$ ☐☐☐☐

Parallel Circuits

PARALLEL CIRCUIT — a circuit where the current has ☐☐☐☐☐☐.

In a parallel circuit, ☐☐☐☐ is not the same ☐☐☐☐☐.

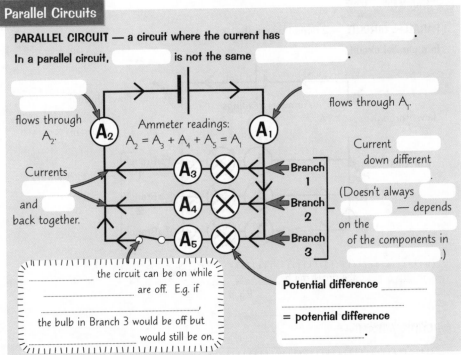

☐☐☐☐ flows through A_2.

flows through A_1.

Ammeter readings:
$A_2 = A_3 + A_4 + A_5 = A_1$

Current ☐☐☐☐ down different ☐☐☐☐.

Currents ☐☐☐☐ and ☐☐☐☐ back together.

A_3 ⊗ ← Branch 1

A_4 ⊗ ← Branch 2

A_5 ⊗ ← Branch 3

(Doesn't always ☐☐☐☐ — depends on the ☐☐☐☐ of the components in ☐☐☐☐.)

_____ the circuit can be on while
_____ are off. E.g. if
_____,
the bulb in Branch 3 would be off but
_____ would still be on.

Potential difference _____

= potential difference _____.

Series and Parallel Circuits

Series Circuits

SERIES CIRCUIT — a circuit where the _____ .

In a series circuit, _____

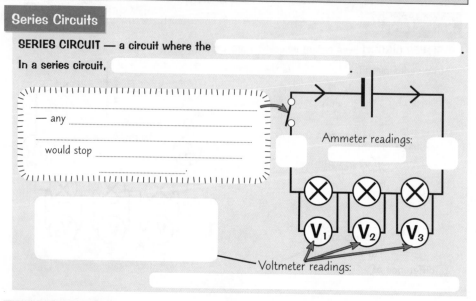

— any _____

would stop _____

Ammeter readings:

Voltmeter readings:

Parallel Circuits

PARALLEL CIRCUIT — a circuit where the _____ .

In a parallel circuit, _____ .

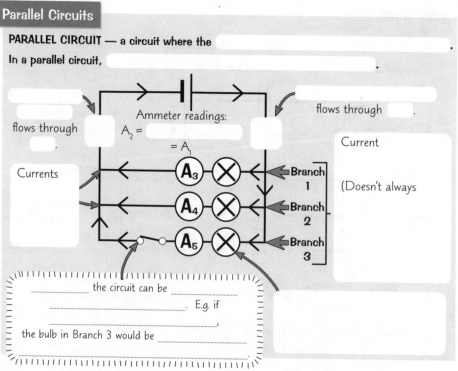

flows through ____

Ammeter readings:

$A_2 =$

$= A_1$

Currents

flows through ____

Current

(Doesn't always

Branch 1

Branch 2

Branch 3

_____ the circuit can be _____ . E.g. if

_____ ,

the bulb in Branch 3 would be _____

Static Electricity and Magnets

Static Charge

Atoms contain both _____
(_____) and positive charges.

Electrons _____ move.
Positive charges _____ move.

When two _____
are rubbed together, _____
are scraped off one object and
_____ . E.g.

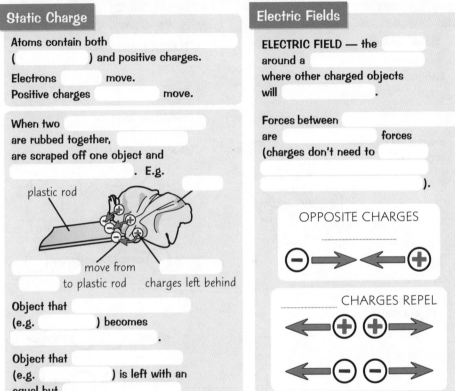

plastic rod

_____ move from
_____ to plastic rod _____ charges left behind

Object that _____
(e.g. _____) becomes
_____ .

Object that _____
(e.g. _____) is left with an
equal but _____ .

Electric Fields

ELECTRIC FIELD — the _____
around a _____
where other charged objects
will _____ .

Forces between _____
are _____ forces
(charges don't need to _____
_____
_____).

OPPOSITE CHARGES

$\ominus \rightarrow \leftarrow \oplus$

CHARGES REPEL

$\leftarrow \oplus \quad \oplus \rightarrow$

$\leftarrow \ominus \quad \ominus \rightarrow$

Bar Magnets

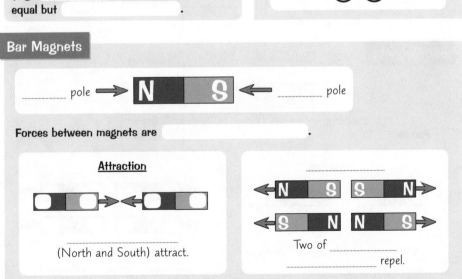

_____ pole ➡ **N** **S** ⬅ _____ pole

Forces between magnets are _____ .

Attraction

_____
(North and South) attract.

Two of _____
_____ repel.

Static Electricity and Magnets

Static Charge

Atoms contain

Electrons

charges

are rubbed together,   are
scraped off

. E.g.

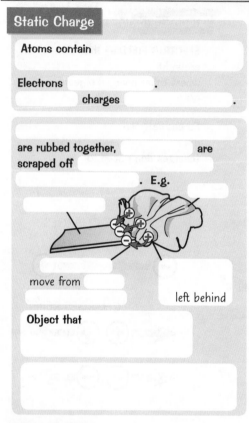

move from

left behind

Object that

Electric Fields

ELECTRIC FIELD —

Forces between

(charges don't need to

).

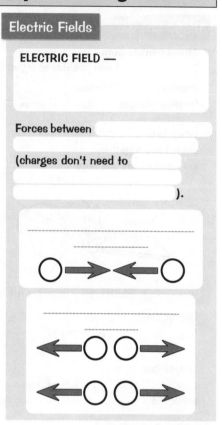

Bar Magnets

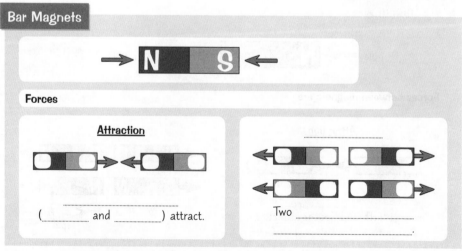

Forces

Attraction

(and   ) attract.

Two

Magnetic Fields and Electromagnets

Magnetic Fields

MAGNETIC FIELD — a region where

_____

(e.g. iron) experience _____ .

MAGNETIC FIELD LINES — lines that are
drawn to show the _____ .

_____

_____

Compasses

Compasses always point from
_____ along
_____ .

Compass _____
_____ in the magnetic field.

The Earth's Magnetic Field

The Earth has a magnetic
field with a _____
_____
_____ .

Compasses point
to the Earth's
_____
_____ .

Maps have an arrow showing
you _____
_____ . So you can use
a map and _____ .

Electromagnets

A current going through a wire causes a
_____ .

ELECTROMAGNET — a magnet made from a _____ .

_____ — coil of wire.

magnetic field
(same as _____)

N ⟵ ⟶ **S**

Current can be _____
_____ , so _____
can be turned on or off.

Three ways to _____
_____ of an electromagnet:

1 More _____ in the wire.

2 More _____ in the coil.

3 _____

A simple _____ is made from a _____ in a
magnetic field. When _____ ,
_____ a magnetic field forms around it. As the _____
_____ a magnetic field, it feels multiple forces, _____ .

Magnetic Fields and Electromagnets

Magnetic Fields

MAGNETIC FIELD —

MAGNETIC FIELD LINES — lines that are

Compasses

Compasses always point

The Earth's Magnetic Field

The Earth has   with a

.

Compasses point

Maps have

So you can use

Electromagnets

.... going through ....

ELECTROMAGNET — a magnet

N ←   → S

Current can be

Three ways to

of an electromagnet:

1   in the wire.

2   in the coil.

3

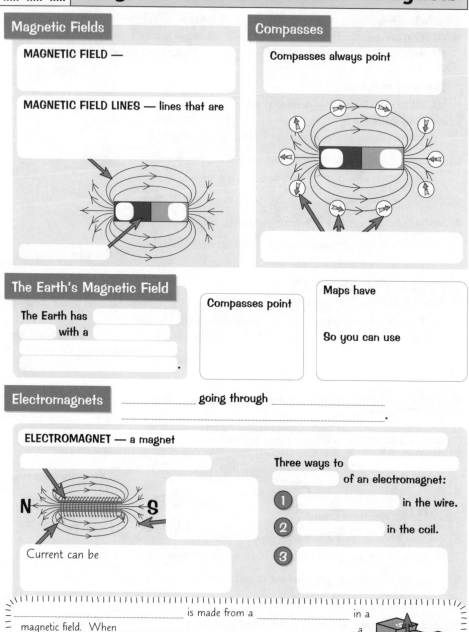

.... is made from a .... in a
magnetic field. When .... , a
magnetic field forms around it. As the .... a magnetic
field, ...

Mixed Practice Quizzes

Quiz time. Have a crack at the following questions, which are all based on p.141-150. If you do them all, I guarantee you'll be a true knowledge magnet.

Quiz 1   Date: ...... / ...... / ......

1) State the relationship between resistance, potential difference and current. ☑

2) Describe the direction in which compasses point when they are placed in the magnetic field of a bar magnet. ☑

3) True or false? A magnetic field is produced around a wire when a current flows through the wire. ☑

4) Define 'series circuit'. ☑

5) What unit is used to measure potential difference? ☑

6) Which component of a circuit is represented in circuit diagrams by a circle with an 'M' in it? ☑

7) What is a solenoid? ☑

8) True or false? A break in a parallel circuit will stop the current flowing everywhere in the circuit. ☑

Total: ☐

Quiz 2   Date: ...... / ...... / ......

1) Do insulators have high or low resistance? ☑

2) True or false? In a series circuit, the potential difference across each component is the same as the potential difference of the cell. ☑

3) What are magnetic field lines? ☑

4) What is 'electric current'? ☑

5) If two objects with the same electric charge were brought near each other, would they attract or repel each other? ☑

6) True or false? Electric current is not used up in circuits. ☑

7) Give an example of an insulator. ☑

8) How is potential difference provided in a circuit? ☑

Total: ☐

Mixed Practice Quizzes

Date: ...... / ...... / ......

1) What is a voltmeter used for?

2) What unit is used to measure resistance?

3) When two insulating objects are rubbed together, one of
   the objects becomes negatively charged. Explain why.

4) State two ways you can increase the strength of an electromagnet.

5) True or false? An electric field is the space around a charged object
   where other charged objects will feel a force.

6) True or false? Magnetic field lines point from South to North.

7) How are ammeters represented in circuit diagrams?

8) What effect does increasing potential difference
   have on current, if resistance stays the same?

Total:

Quiz 4   Date: ...... / ...... / ......

1) What is an electromagnet?

2) True or false? On circuit diagrams, current is
   shown as moving from positive to negative.

3) What is a conductor?

4) True or false? A magnetic field is a region
   where magnetic objects feel a force.

5) What does the potential difference rating of a bulb tell you?

6) Define 'parallel circuit'.

7) What unit is used to measure current?

8) What do compasses point towards in Earth's magnetic field?

Total:

Gravity, The Sun, Stars & Light Years

First Go:
...... / ...... / ......

Gravity and Weight

GRAVITY — a _____ that exists between all masses.

Gravity is a _____ (masses _____ for the force to act).

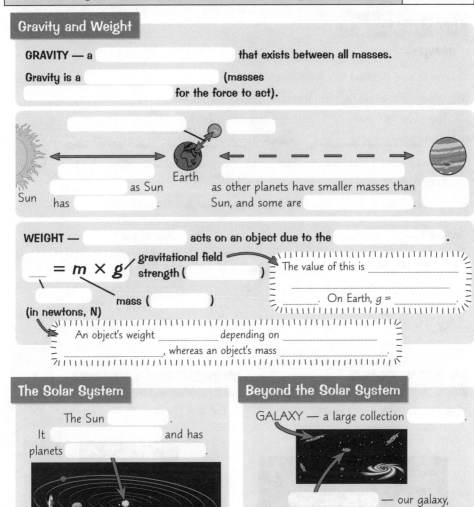

_____

_____ as Sun has _____.

Earth

Sun

as other planets have smaller masses than Sun, and some are _____.

WEIGHT — _____ acts on an object due to the _____.

$$\text{\_\_\_\_} = m \times g$$

gravitational field strength (_____)

mass (_____)

(in newtons, N)

The value of this is _____
_____. On Earth, $g =$ _____.

An object's weight _____ depending on _____, whereas an object's mass _____.

The Solar System

The Sun _____.

It _____ and has planets _____.

_____ keeps planets in orbit.

Beyond the Solar System

GALAXY — a large collection _____.

_____ — our galaxy, which contains _____ and other stars, e.g. _____.

There are _____ in a galaxy, and billions of galaxies in _____.

Light Years

LIGHT YEAR — _____ one year.

Light years are used for _____.

Gravity, The Sun, Stars & Light Years

Gravity and Weight

GRAVITY —

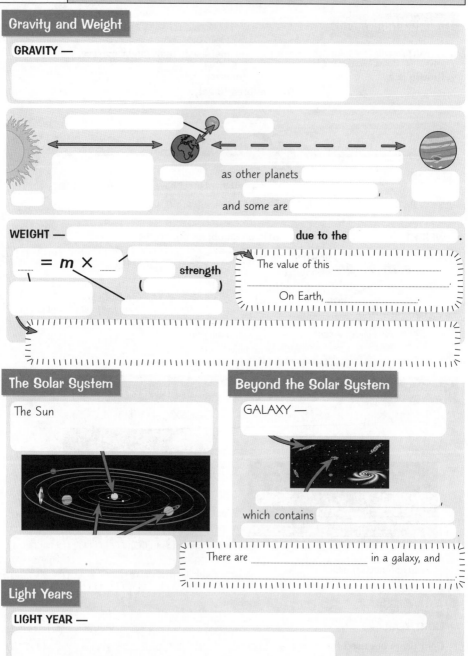

as other planets

and some are

WEIGHT — due to the

$...... = m \times ......$

( ) strength

The value of this

On Earth,

The Solar System

The Sun

Beyond the Solar System

GALAXY —

which contains

There are in a galaxy, and

Light Years

LIGHT YEAR —

Day and Night and the Four Seasons

Day and Night

_____ = time it takes the Earth to complete one rotation about its axis = _____

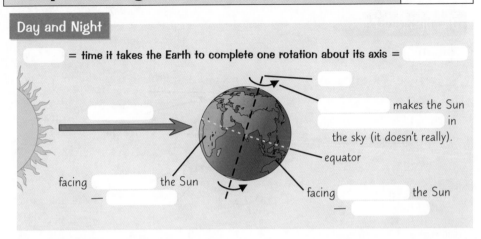

_____ makes the Sun _____ in the sky (it doesn't really).

equator

facing __ _____ the Sun

facing __ _____ the Sun

The Seasons

1 year = the time it takes the Earth to orbit the Sun once = _____

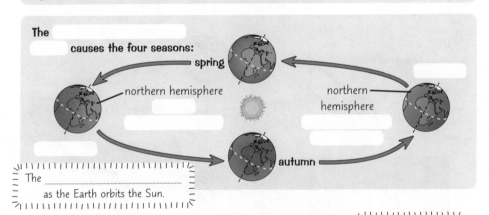

The _____ _____ causes the four seasons:

spring

northern hemisphere

northern hemisphere

autumn

The _____ as the Earth orbits the Sun.

When _____ _____ _____ _____ in the southern hemisphere (and vice versa).

In summer...	In winter...
more time in sunlight (_____ longer than _____)	less time in sunlight (_____ shorter than _____)
sunlight _____ smaller area	sunlight _____ larger area

Day and Night and the Four Seasons

Day and Night

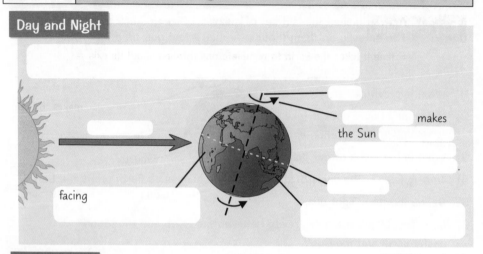

facing

makes
the Sun

The Seasons

1 year = ...

....

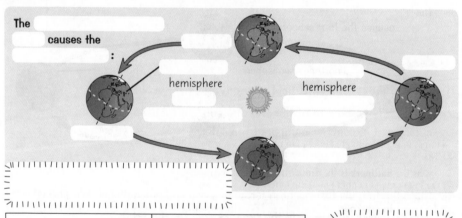

The

causes the :

hemisphere

hemisphere

.... in sunlight	.... in sunlight
(	(
...................)	...................)
sunlight	sunlight ....
....	....

When ....
....
....
....
....
(and vice versa).

Mixed Practice Quizzes

Amazing! You've reached the last set of quizzes. Give yourself a pat on the back. Don't forget to actually do them though — they'll test you on p.153-156.

Quiz 1   Date: ...... / ...... / ......

1) What is gravity?

2) How many hours does it take for the Earth to complete one rotation about its axis?

3) What is the name of our galaxy?

4) True or false? The angle of the Earth's tilt changes as Earth orbits the Sun.

5) Define the term 'light year'.

6) Is there a bigger force of gravity between the Earth and the Moon or the Earth and the Sun?

7) True or false? Gravity only exists between planets and stars.

8) When the northern hemisphere is tilted towards the Sun, is it summer or winter in the northern hemisphere?

Total:

Quiz 2   Date: ...... / ...... / ......

1) What is the gravitational field strength on Earth, in N/kg?

2) Describe how the size of the area the sunlight focuses on is different in summer compared to winter.

3) If it's winter in the northern hemisphere, what season is it in the southern hemisphere?

4) State the formula for weight in terms of mass and gravitational field strength.

5) True or false? One year is the time it takes for the Earth to complete one full orbit of the Sun.

6) True or false? The Sun is a star.

7) What is a galaxy?

8) Describe how the rotation of the Earth leads to day time and night time.

Total:

Mixed Practice Quizzes

Quiz 3   Date: ...... / ...... / ......

1) Define 'weight'.

2) True or false? An object's mass changes depending on where it is in the Universe.

3) How many days does it take for the Earth to orbit the Sun (to the nearest 1 day)?

4) True or false? There are billions of galaxies in the Universe.

5) If you are on the side of the Earth facing away from the Sun, is it day time or night time?

6) Is gravity a contact or non-contact force?

7) What name is given to the imaginary line that the Earth rotates about?

8) What are light years used for?

Total:

Quiz 4   Date: ...... / ...... / ......

1) True or false? It takes the Earth one day to complete a rotation about its axis.

2) What property of the Earth's axis causes the seasons?

3) What do the planets in the Solar System orbit?

4) In which season, summer or winter, are days shorter than nights?

5) True or false? Gravitational field strength is the same everywhere.

6) Why does the Sun appear to move in the sky over the course of a day?

7) What name is given to the force of attraction that exists between all masses?

8) Explain why there is a bigger force of gravity between the Earth and the Sun than between the Earth and any other planet in the solar system.

Total:

SHNR31